The Open
University

Business School

Unit 5

Quantitative methods
for management accounting

Written by Elizabeth R Porter

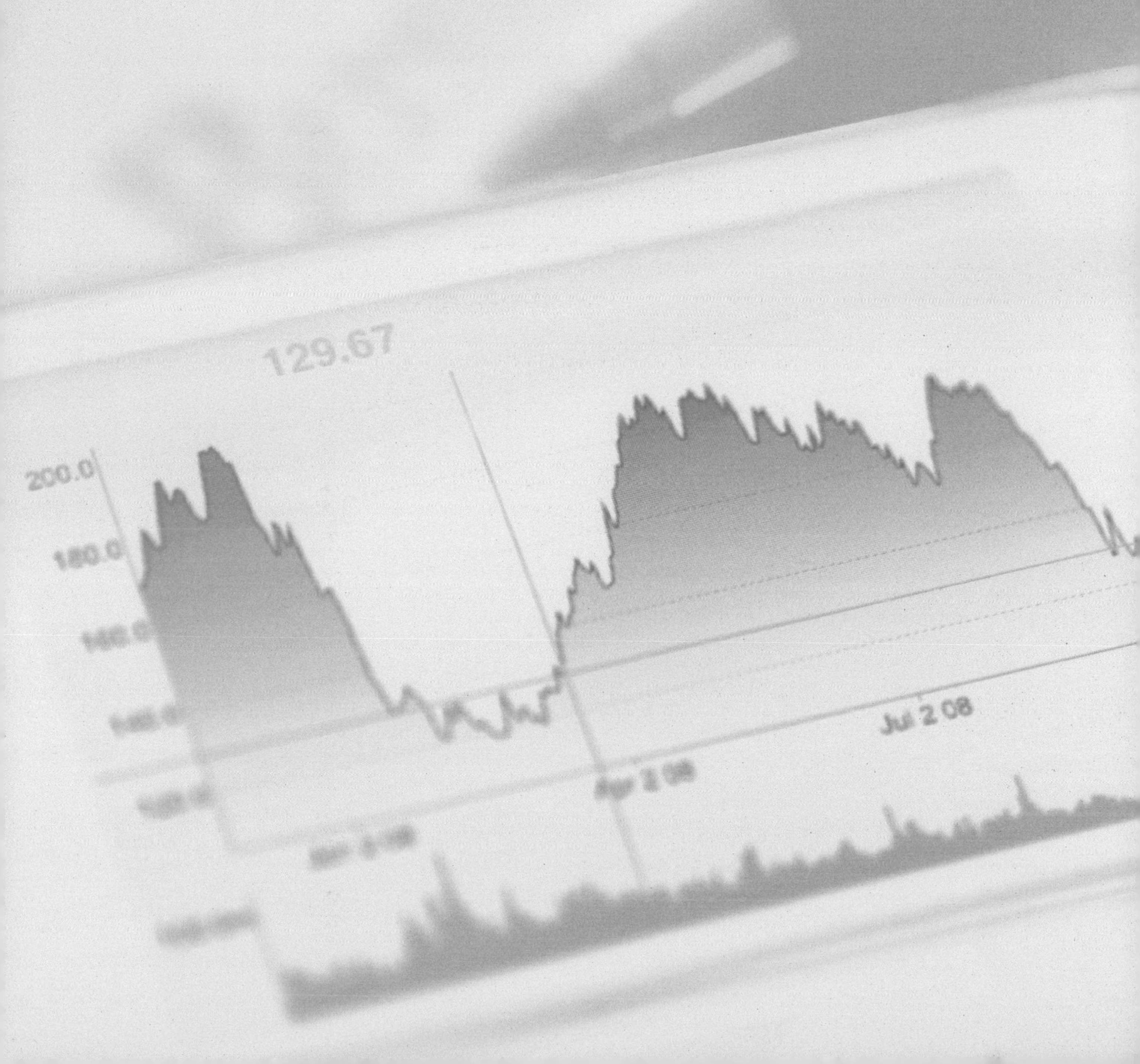

129.67

200.0

180.0

Jul 2 08

Module Team

Dr Mike Lucas, *B292 Chair & Author*
Professor Jane Frecknall-Hughes, *Professional Certificate in Accounting Chair & Author*
Elizabeth R Porter, *Regional Manager & Author*
Jonathan Winship, *Author*
Stuart Munro, *Author*
Dr Vira Krakhmal, *Author*
Dr Pauline Gleadle, *Author*
Dr Jane Hughes, *Contributor*
Sam Cooper, *Programme Coordinator*
Emir Forken, *Programme Manager*
Dr Lesley Messer, *Head of Curriculum Operations*
Funmi Mapelujo, *Qualifications Manager*
Kelly Dobbs, *Curriculum Assistant*

External Assessor

Professor Stuart Turley, Manchester Business School

Critical Readers

Richard Davies
Dr Jane Hughes

Developmental Testers

Dr Teodora Burnand
Sam Cooper
Diane Jamieson
Sue Winship
Nicole Wright

Production Team

Simon Ashby, *Media Developer*
Martin Brazier, *Media Developer*
Anne Brown, *Media Assistant*
Vicky Eves, *Media Developer*
Diane Hopwood, *Rights Assistant*
Lee Johnson, *Media Project Manager*
Siggy Martin, *Print Buyer*
Kelvin Street, *Library*
Keith Wakeman, *Service Administrator*

The Module Team wishes to acknowledge the use of some materials from B680 *The Certificate in Accounting*.

This publication forms part of the Open University module B292 *Management accounting*. Details of this and other Open University modules can be obtained from the Student Registration and Enquiry Service, The Open University, PO Box 197, Milton Keynes MK7 6BJ, United Kingdom (tel. +44 (0)845 300 60 90; email general-enquiries@open.ac.uk).

Alternatively, you may visit the Open University website at www.open.ac.uk where you can learn more about the wide range of modules and packs offered at all levels by The Open University.

To purchase a selection of Open University materials visit www.ouw.co.uk, or contact Open University Worldwide, Walton Hall, Milton Keynes MK7 6AA, United Kingdom for a brochure (tel. +44 (0)1908 858793; fax +44 (0)1908 858787; email ouw-customer-services@open.ac.uk).

The Open University

Walton Hall

Milton Keynes

MK7 6AA

First published 2011. Second edition 2012.

Edited and designed by The Open University.

Typeset in India by OKS Prepress Services, Chennai.

Printed in the United Kingdom by Cambrian Printers, Aberystwyth.

FSC
Mixed Sources
Product group from well-managed forests and other controlled sources
Cert no. TT-COC-2200
www.fsc.org
© 1996 Forest Stewardship Council

ISBN 978 1780 0 7384 2

2.1

Contents

Introduction   **5**

            Learning aims and outcomes of Unit 5   9

Session 1   **Basic numerical skills required for accounting**   **11**

            Introduction   11

            1.1 Using BODMAS and brackets to solve calculations   12

            1.2 Using the memory function in a scientific calculator   14

            1.3 Rounding   16

            1.4 Fractions   17

            1.5 Ratios   19

            1.6 Percentages   21

            1.7 Negative numbers   23

            1.8 Tests of reasonableness   25

            1.9 Powers and roots   26

            1.10 Simple equations   29

            1.11 Simultaneous equations   31

            Summary   33

Session 2   **Summarising, presenting and analysing data**   **35**

            Introduction   35

            2.1 Tables   35

            2.2 Charts and graphs   36

            2.3 Constructing charts and graphs using a spreadsheet   41

            2.4 Frequency distributions   49

            2.5 Histograms   50

            2.6 Measures of centrality   51

            2.7 Measures of dispersion   58

            Summary   67

Session 3   **Correlation, regression and forecasting**   **69**

            Introduction   69

            3.1 Dependent and independent variables   69

            3.2 Correlation coefficient (r)   70

            3.3 Coefficient of determination (r^2)   73

            3.4 The scatter graph method   74

            3.5 Regression analysis – the least squares method   74

            3.6 Forecasting   77

            3.7 Time series analysis   78

            Summary   86

Session 4   **Risk and uncertainty in management decision making**   **87**

Introduction   87

4.1 Probability   87

4.2 Expected values   94

4.3 Normal distribution   97

4.4 Decision making under uncertainty   105

Summary   107

Session 5   **Financial mathematics and investment appraisal**   **109**

Introduction   109

5.1 Simple and compound interest   109

5.2 The present value of a future sum of money   111

5.3 Present value of an annuity   112

5.4 An introduction to capital investment appraisal   113

5.5 Accounting rate of return (ARR)   114

5.6 Payback period method   117

5.7 Net present value (NPV)   119

5.8 Internal rate of return (IRR)   124

5.9 Relevant costs and revenues   129

5.10 Practical considerations in capital investment appraisal   132

Summary   134

Session 6   **The role of spreadsheets in accounting**   **137**

Introduction   137

6.1 The nature, benefits and limitations of spreadsheets and the use of spreadsheets in accounting   137

6.2 The fundamentals of spreadsheets   138

6.3 Constructing a multi-sheet cash flow projection statement   142

6.4 Using a multi-sheet spreadsheet to calculate master budgets   152

Summary   165

Unit summary   **166**

Self-assessed Questions   **167**

Acknowledgements   **174**

Introduction

A number of management accounting activities requires skills in numeracy, data analysis and presentation, and knowledge of statistical methods and financial mathematics. This unit is intended to provide you with such skills and quantitative knowledge.

The unit consists of six sessions.

- **Session 1** looks at some of the basic principles of the numerical skills required for management accounting.

- **Session 2** introduces the common quantitative methods for summarising, presenting and analysing data used by management accountants.

- **Session 3** looks at the relationship between variables and how knowledge of the relationship can be used in forecasting. It also looks at the use of time series analysis to reveal a trend masked by seasonal fluctuations.

- **Session 4** looks at the techniques that can be used to provide management information where there is risk or uncertainty. The techniques covered are assigning probabilities to events or items, calculating expected values using the normal distribution curve, and three quantitative approaches to dealing with uncertainty (Maximax, Maximin and Minimax Regret).

- **Session 5** looks at capital investment appraisal as a management accounting technique. It is used to provide information to assist management in making long-term investment decisions such as whether to replace a piece of machinery and with one rather than another where there is choice of machines.

- **Session 6** looks at how spreadsheets can be used and constructed to analyse and present management information.

For this unit you will need a scientific calculator and access to a spreadsheet program.

Unless indicated otherwise, you should spend no more than 15 minutes on the activities in this unit. Some may, indeed, take considerably less than this.

Scientific calculator

Any Casio scientific calculator with a 'natural display' is suitable, as it allows the mathematical formula to be displayed. The two line display shows both your calculation and the answer. These calculators are not expensive and are readily available at a number of supermarkets and high street shops.

If you are not familiar with this type of calculator, using it may at first seem daunting. Do not worry, as there are some instructions for using the Casio fx-83ES, and compatible models, in this unit. Any other scientific calculator is also acceptable provided that you know how to use it, and you have access to the appropriate calculator manual (these are often available to download from the manufacturer's website).

Please note that for the B292 end of module examination, you must use the type of calculator that is permitted by The Open University Examinations Office for this examination.

The permitted type is a non-programmable, that is, basic scientific, calculator. The Casio fx-83ES used for demonstration purposes in this unit is such a basic scientific calculator. There are many others. It is *your* responsibility to make sure that your calculator complies with the regulations.

Note that programmable calculators (including graphics calculators) may not be used.

Figure 1 shows the different parts of the Casio fx-83ES calculator.

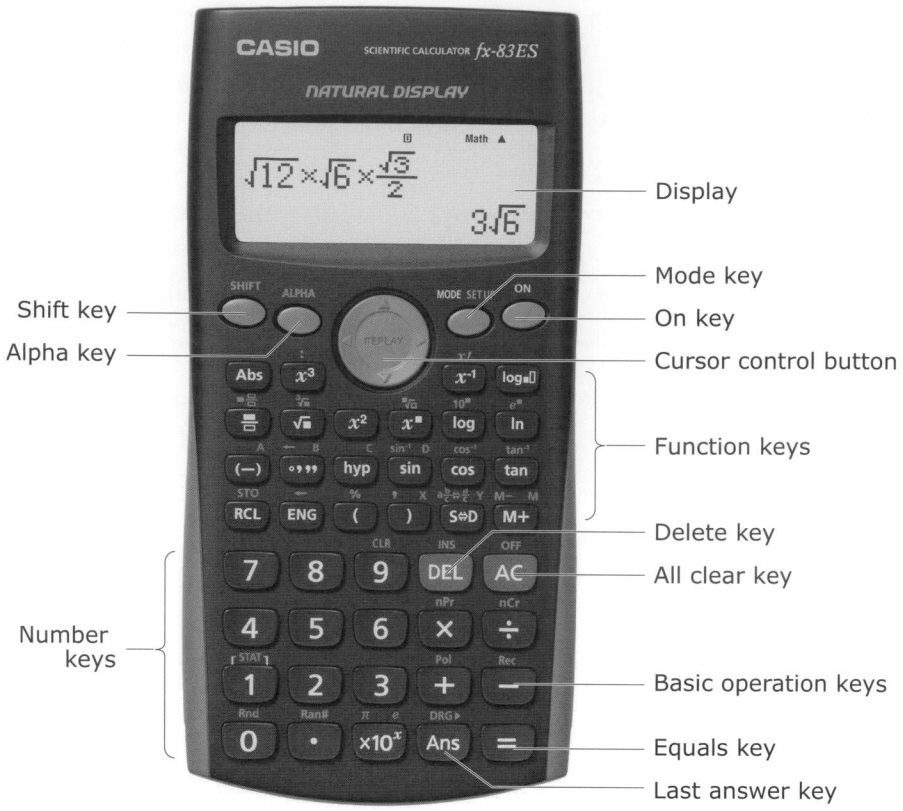

Figure 1   The Casio fx-83ES calculator

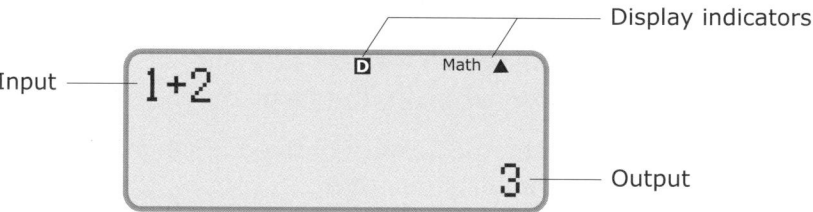

Figure 2   The calculator display

Note: when writing your assignments (TMAs) and your examination answers, it is important that you show all your workings for numerical answers. The marker cannot give you marks if your final answer is incorrect. If, however, you show all your workings (despite having a wrong answer), you may obtain some of the marks for using the correct method.

Many keys on the calculator have more than one use. The main function of a key is printed in white on the key itself. The second function of the key is printed in yellow above the key, and is accessed by pressing the [SHIFT] button before pressing the key. When you press the [SHIFT] button, the symbol 'S' appears at the top left-hand corner of the calculator display to remind you that the button has been pressed. It disappears when you press another key. Some keys also have a third function, printed above the key in red. These functions allow numerical values stored in the calculator memories to be used within calculations and are accessed by pressing the [ALPHA] button before the appropriate key. When the [ALPHA] button is pressed, the symbol 'A' is shown at the top of the calculator display.

The large round button is known as the cursor control button. It is labelled with the word '*REPLAY*'. The ◀ and ▶ keys on this cursor control button enable you to move the cursor (shown on the display as '|') within a calculation on the calculator screen. This is explained later in the box entitled 'Scientific calculator: making corrections'.

Common operations

To	Key sequence
Turn on	[ON]
Turn off	[SHIFT] [AC] *(OFF)*
	Note that the calculator will automatically turn off if not used for about six minutes.
Adjust the display contrast	[SHIFT] [MODE] *(SETUP)* ▼ [5] *(◀CONT▶)* then use ◀ and ▶ to adjust, and press [AC] when finished.
Restore the factory settings	[SHIFT] [9] *(CLR)* [1] *(Setup)* [=] *(Yes)* [AC]
Clear the contents of all memories	[SHIFT] [9] *(CLR)* [2] *(Memory)* [=] *(Yes)* [AC]
Restore the default settings and clear all memories	[SHIFT] [9] *(CLR)* [3] *(All)* [=] *(Yes)* [AC]
Cancel a calculation, or exit menus	[AC]
Obtain an answer	[=]
Obtain a decimal answer in Math mode	[SHIFT] [=]
Toggle between exact and decimal answers in Math mode	[S↔D]
Use the result of the previous calculation...	[Ans]
...e.g., to find 42 minus the previous result	[4] [2] [−] [Ans] [=]
Store a value in 'M' memory	[SHIFT] [RCL] *(STO)* [M+] (M)
Add a value to that in the 'M' memory	[M+]
Subtract a value from that in the 'M' memory	[SHIFT] [M+] (M−)
Display the value stored in the 'M' memory	[RCL] [M+] (M)
Use the value in the 'M' memory in a calculation	[ALPHA] [M+] (M)

Scientific calculator: initialising your calculator

To initialise your scientific calculator to the default module settings, turn it on and then enter the following two key sequences:

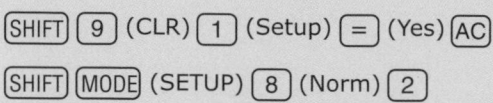

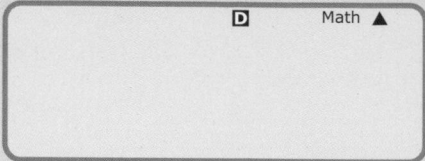

Your calculator will now be working in 'Math' mode, and the word Math will be shown near the right-hand side of the top of the calculator display:

D	Math ▲

Figure 3   The calculator display showing math mode

Math mode is the recommended way of using your calculator during this module as it allows mathematics to be entered and displayed in a similar way to how you would write it on paper.

Scientific calculator keys you will need to use

To enter	Key sequence
-2	$(-)$ 2 or $-$ 2
3^2	3 x^2 or 3 $x^■$ 2
4^3	4 x^3 or 4 $x^■$ 3
5^4	5 $x^■$ 4
$\sqrt{3}$	$\sqrt{■}$ 3
$\sqrt[3]{4}$	SHIFT $\sqrt{■}$ $(^3\sqrt{■})$ 4
$\sqrt[4]{5}$	SHIFT $x^■$ $(^■\sqrt{□})$ 4 ▶ 5
$\frac{2}{3}$	In Math mode ▤ 2 ▼ 3
S↔D	In Math mode, will enable you to toggle between exact and decimal answers

Spreadsheet

A **spreadsheet** is a tool for calculating, analysing and manipulating figures. It makes calculations quicker and easier and it is used for sorting, filtering and categorising large volumes of information.

It can be thought of as an electronic piece of paper (worksheet) divided into columns which are numbered A, B, C, etc., and rows which are numbered 1, 2, 3, etc. Where a column intersects a row it is called a cell. Each cell has an address. For example, the cell A1 is where column A intersects row 1. The active cell is the one where the cursor is.

Spreadsheets can be used throughout this unit and Session 6 looks at the role of spreadsheets in accounting. There are several spreadsheets on the market, although Excel is the most widely used and this is the spreadsheet referred to in Unit 5. References to Excel commands are to Excel 2003. If you are using another version, they may be slightly different.

Assessment formulae

The following formulae will be given to you in your examination.

Arithmetic mean of an ungrouped frequency distribution

$$\bar{x} = \frac{\sum x}{n}$$

Arithmetic mean of a grouped frequency distribution

$$\bar{x} = A + \frac{\sum fd}{\sum f} \text{ or } \bar{x} = \frac{\sum fx}{\sum f}$$

The standard deviation of ungrouped data

$$\sigma = \sqrt{\frac{\sum (x - \bar{x})^2}{n}}$$

The standard deviation of a frequency distribution

$$\sigma = \sqrt{\frac{\sum f(x - \bar{x})^2}{\sum f}}$$

The standard deviation of a grouped frequency distribution

$$\sigma = \sqrt{\frac{\sum f(x - \bar{x})^2}{\sum f}}$$

Standard deviation of a sample

$$s = \sqrt{\frac{\sum (x - \bar{x})^2}{n - 1}}$$

Coefficient of variation

$$\frac{\sigma}{\bar{x}} \times 100$$

Coefficient of variation of a sample

$$\frac{s}{x} \times 100$$

Correlation coefficient

$$r = \frac{n\sum xy - \sum x \sum y}{\sqrt{\left[n\sum x^2 - (\sum x)^2 \right]\left[n\sum y^2 - (\sum y)^2 \right]}}$$

Regression analysis

Equation 1: $\sum y = an + b\sum x$

Equation 2: $\sum xy = a\sum x + b\sum x^2$

or

$$a = \frac{\sum y - b\sum x}{n} \text{ and}$$

$$b = \frac{n\sum xy - \sum x \sum y}{n\sum x^2 - (\sum x)^2}$$

Trend

The additive method: $A = T + S$

The multiplicative method: $S = A/T$

Normal distribution

$$z = \frac{x - \mu}{\sigma}$$

These may appear quite daunting at this stage, but you will learn to use them as you progress through Unit 5.

Learning aims and outcomes of Unit 5

Upon completion of Unit 5, you are expected to be able to understand relevant quantitative methods in management accounting which relate to:

1 basic numerical skills required for accounting
2 summarising, presenting and analysing data
3 correlation, linear regression analysis and linear forecasting
4 risk and uncertainty in management decision making
5 financial mathematics and capital investment appraisal
6 the role of spreadsheets in accounting.

SESSION 1 Basic numerical skills required for accounting

Introduction

Upon completion of Session 1, you are expected to be able to:

- use BODMAS and brackets to perform calculations
- use the memory function in a scientific calculator
- be able to understand and use the following aspects of numeracy: rounding, fractions, ratios, percentages, negative numbers, powers and roots, and the test of reasonableness
- use a table of equivalencies
- solve and manipulate simple equations.

This session looks at some of the basic principles of the numerical skills required for management accounting.

Accountants do not need to be experts in mathematics, although they should be able to add, subtract, multiply, divide and handle fractions, ratios, roots and powers as well as solve simple equations.

In today's world many people use calculators or computers to avoid the tedious process of performing calculations in their head or on paper. However, using a calculator or computer does require certain skills in understanding the functions which the buttons perform and the order in which to carry out the calculations. It is hoped that you will also develop your mental arithmetic skills.

Your need to study the material in this section is dependent on your mathematical background. If you are weak or rusty on basic arithmetic or maths, you should find the material in this session particularly helpful.

All calculators are designed to carry out four basic operations:

- addition $9 + 52 = 61$
- subtraction $52 - 9 = 43$
- multiplication $12 \times 4 = 48$
- division $12 \div 4 = 3$

Scientific calculator: basic operation

Basic calculations are entered into the scientific calculator in exactly the same order as they are written on paper, as demonstrated in Activity 1.1. The calculator displays the calculations that you enter. When you press $\boxed{=}$ the answer is displayed at the bottom right of the screen.

If you find that any instructions contained in this material do not produce the expected answer, please look at the instructions for your calculator and adapt your actions accordingly.

Scientific calculator: making corrections

Errors in pressing calculator keys (entering a key sequence) can be corrected using the editing facilities to correct your error.

The ◀ and ▶ keys on the large cursor control button (labelled with the word '*REPLAY*') enable you to move the cursor (shown on the display as '|') within a calculation on the calculator screen.

Characters can then be inserted at the cursor location simply by pressing the appropriate buttons, and items to the left of the cursor can be deleted using the DEL key. This can be done either before or after the = key has been pressed. To re-evaluate an edited calculation, simply press = at any time.

In some circumstances, however, it may be easier to abandon what you have typed and start again, by pressing the 'all clear' AC key!

If a serious error is made when entering a calculation into the calculator, it may prevent the answer being calculated at all, as the calculation may not make mathematical sense. In such circumstances a 'Syntax ERROR' message will be displayed as:

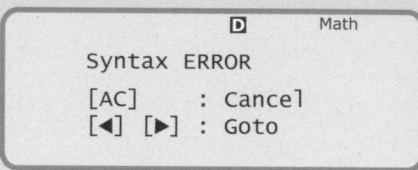

Figure 4   The calculator display showing a syntax error

The Syntax ERROR screen gives you two options:

(1) Press AC to abandon the calculation and clear the screen
(2) Press either ◀ or ▶ to return to the erroneous calculation with the editing cursor placed at the point of the error, ready for a correction to be made.

Other types of calculator error that you may encounter are:

'Math ERROR', when the calculation you entered appears to make mathematical sense but the result cannot be calculated, such as attempting to divide by zero, or when the result is too large for the calculator to handle.

'Stack ERROR', when your calculation is too complex to be handled in one attempt. In such circumstances, try to break the calculation into a number of simpler ones.

In these cases, the calculator will display a screen similar to that for the Syntax ERROR, allowing you either to abandon or to correct your calculation.

Now practise correcting some mistakes. You might like to play with the figures at the start of Session 1.

1.1 Using BODMAS and brackets to solve calculations

When several operations are combined, the order in which they are performed is important. For example, $3 + 6 \times 21$ might be interpreted as:

- add 3 to 6 then multiply the answer by 21 to get 189; or
- multiply 21 by 6 then add on 3 to get 129.

The acronym BODMAS gives a way of remembering the sequence of rules to be applied so that the correct answer is obtained:

(B) Brackets

(O) Order (This means raising to a power, which will be explained later.)

(D) Division

(M) Multiplication

(A) Addition

(S) Subtraction

Using BODMAS in the example, multiplication should be carried out before addition; therefore the correct answer is 129.

Looking at the terms used in BODMAS all but the first two terms are self evident:

- **Brackets** should be used to show the order of calculation. Therefore $3 + 6 \times 21$ becomes $3 + (6 \times 21) = 129$.

- **Order** is a term that may not be familiar to you. It is used here as another word for 'power'. The number 5 to the power of 5 is $5 \times 5 \times 5 \times 5 \times 5$ and is written 5^5. (This is covered in more detail in Section 1.9.)

Activity 1.1 ....

Practise using BODMAS to answer the following, without using your calculator:

(a) $144 \div 12 - 7$

(b) $103 + 2 \times 14$

(c) $5 \times (147 - 132)$

(d) $(19 + 3) \times (17 - 12)$

Now use your calculator to work out the answers to the following calculations (note: your calculator uses BODMAS when producing the answer):

(e) 4,257 ÷ 87 − 29

(f) 1,728 + 96 × 153

(g) 54 × (1,293 − 971)

(h) (1,023 + 1,346) × (56,872 − 42,956)

You may notice that in (h) the calculation was too long to fit on the scientific calculator display. In such circumstances the symbol '◀' or '▶' appears at the left or right of the display to indicate that there is more information in that direction. This information can be seen by scrolling using the left or right side of the large cursor control button located under the calculator screen.

If you type a very long calculation into your calculator, then you may see the cursor (which is usually shown as '■'). This means that you are allowed to type only 10 more characters. If you encounter this, you should break your calculation into smaller parts.

Fractions or decimals?

Earlier you set up your calculator to use Math mode. In this mode, when the result of a calculation is not a whole number, it will be displayed as a fraction, such as $\frac{2}{3}$, wherever possible. To obtain the answer in decimal form, you need to press (SHIFT) = instead of =. Alternatively, you can toggle between the fraction (fractions are discussed in Section 1.4) and decimal output using the (S-D) key.

Feedback

Here are the answers you should have obtained:

(a) 144 ÷ 12 − 7 = 5

(b) 103 + 2 × 14 = 131

(c) 5 × (147 − 132) = 75

(d) (19 + 3) × (17 − 12) = 110

Here are the answers you should have obtained using your scientific calculator:

(e) 4,257 ÷ 87 − 29 = 19.93103448

   Note that the calculator uses the BODMAS rule.

(f) 1,728 + 96 × 153 = 16,416

(g) 54 × (1,293 − 971) = 17,388

(h) (1,023 + 1,346) × (56,872 − 42,956) = 32,967,004

1.2 Using the memory function in a scientific calculator

The scientific calculator memory is particularly useful when you want to calculate the values of several expressions that have a common part. This common part needs be entered only once and its value reused several times subsequently. For example, with the expression $(x+3)^2$ you can see that no matter what the values of x, the formula always requires the calculation of $(x+3)^2$. It might be efficient to calculate the value of $(x+3)^2$ once, store it in memory and reuse this value in the subsequent calculations. When preparing an income statement, the gross profit can be calculated and stored in the memory; then the other costs can be added, before deducting them from the gross profit figure you have stored in the memory.

The calculator has several different memories ('A', 'B', 'C', 'D', 'M', 'X' and 'Y'). Only the 'M' memory will be considered, as it is the only one you will need during this module. The 'M' memory is accessed using the [M+] key (and its associated functions) at the bottom right-hand corner of the function key area.

Before using the calculator memory, it is good practice always to clear any previous data stored in the calculator using the key sequence [SHIFT] [9] (CLR) [2] (Memory) [=] (Yes) [AC]. Note that this clears all the calculator memories.

To store the result of an expression just calculated (i.e., an answer displayed in the output area of the calculator screen) in the 'M' calculator memory, use the key sequence [SHIFT] [RCL] (STO) [M+] (M). Here the second function of the [RCL] (or recall) button, which is called 'STO' (or store), is being used. After selecting the store function, you need to tell the calculator the memory in which the value is to be stored. These memories are labelled in red on some of the calculator keys and the 'M' memory is obtained by pressing the [M+] key. The key sequence can be read as 'store the current result into the M memory'.

To display the current contents of the 'M' memory, press [RCL] [M+] (M). The value stored in memory can also be used as part of a subsequent calculation by inserting the letter M into the appropriate point of the expression [ALPHA] [M+] (M). For example, to find the square of the value currently stored in the 'M' memory, M^2, use the key sequence [ALPHA] [M+] (M) [x^2] [=].

When there is a value stored in the 'M' memory, the display indicator M is shown at the top of the display.

Activity 1.2 ....

Often a management accountant will wish to see the weekly cost of a particular type of expense. Use the memory function on your scientific calculator to store the value of $\frac{1}{52}$ in the 'M' memory of the calculator and then use this stored value to find the value of $1.5 \times 0.92^2 \times \frac{1}{52}$ to 3 decimal places.

Feedback ....

To find the value of $1.5 \times 0.92^2 \times \frac{1}{52}$ to 3 decimal places, work out the value of $\frac{1}{52}$ by using the key sequence: [▤] 1 [▼] 52 [SHIFT] = and store it in the 'M' memory using the key sequence [SHIFT] [RCL] (STO) [M+] (M).

This value can then be used to find the final result using:

$1.5 \times 0.92 \boxed{x^2} \times$ ALPHA M+ (M) =, which gives you 0.02441538462; rounding to 3 decimal places gives 0.024. (Note after pressing = you may need to press S↔D.)

Other 'M' memory operations

The value stored in the 'M' memory can also be changed by adding or subtracting the result of a further calculation, as indicated below.

- To add the result of the latest calculation to the value currently in the memory, press M+.

- To subtract the value of the latest calculation from the value currently in the memory, use the key sequence SHIFT M+ (M-).

Expressions can also be stored in, added to or subtracted from the memory at the same time as they are evaluated by replacing the = at the end of a calculation with one of the above key sequences. For example, to calculate 43 – 16 and store the result straight into the memory, use the following key sequence:

4 3 – 1 6 SHIFT RCL (STO) M+ (M).

1.3 Rounding

The level of precision required in performing calculations varies from business to business. A house builder may price a new house to the nearest £10,000. To an electricity supplier price differences of less than one penny per unit will be significant.

The finance director of a large supermarket would see goods priced in pounds and pence. However, budgets may be in thousands of pounds (£'000) and the annual accounts in millions of pounds (£'000,000).

1.3.1 Rule of rounding

If the digit to round is below 5, round down. If the digit is 5 or above, round up.

When rounding to two decimal places look at the third digit after the decimal point. If that figure is 5 or above, round up the second digit to the next highest figure. For example, 3.436 will become 3.44. If the figure is lower than 5, that figure is dropped so 3.434 will become 3.43.

Further examples of rounding to two decimal places (d.p.):

3.33333 rounds to 3.33

17.346 rounds to 17.35

21.345 rounds to 21.35

368.24567 rounds to 368.25

Activity 1.3 ....

Not all figures need the same degree of accuracy, so you may wish to round some figures, for example, when preparing budgets.

Round 54.54377 to:

(a) 2 decimal places   (b)   3 decimal places
(c) the nearest whole number.

Feedback ....

(a) The answer must contain two decimal digits so you need to look at the third decimal digit (3) and round up or down accordingly. As 3 is less than 5, round down, so 54.54377 rounds to 54.54.

(b) Look at the fourth decimal digit. As 7 is more than 5, round up, so 54.54377 rounds to 54.544.

(c) To round to the nearest whole number, look at the first decimal digit and decide whether to round up or down. Here, 54.54377 rounds to 55.

1.3.2 Rounding to a specific number of significant figures

Rounding to a given number of decimal places is not the only form of rounding used. There will be situations when rounding to a specific number of **significant figures (s.f.)** is needed. In this form of rounding:

7.7754 will round to 7.8 to two significant figures

1,475.9684 will round to 1,480 to three significant figures

1.26385 will round to 1.264 to four significant figures

0.004672 will round to 0.00467 to five significant figures

The rule for rounding up or down is the same as in the earlier case of rounding to a certain number of decimal places. The significant figures part of the rounding process indicates how many digits (figures) to include, and ignores any trailing zeros present after the decimal point.

1.4 Fractions

Up until now, numbers have only been looked at in terms of their decimal notation, for example, 8.546, but this is not the only way of representing numbers.

A **fraction** is a number that describes the relationship between part of something and the whole. If the two partners in a business decide to share profits equally, each partner will get one half of the available profit and this is represented by the symbol $\frac{1}{2}$.

A fraction is a ratio of two numbers, for example, $\frac{1}{2}, \frac{2}{3}, \frac{4}{5}$. To turn them into decimals you divide the top half (known as the **numerator**) by the bottom half (known as the **denominator**):

$$\frac{\text{numerator}}{\text{denominator}}$$

A fraction can have many different but equivalent representations, for example, $\frac{1}{2}, \frac{2}{4}, \frac{8}{16}$ all represent the same fraction.

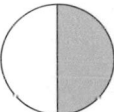 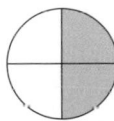 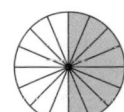

Figure 5 Fractions of a circle

It is usual to write a fraction in its lowest terms, by dividing the top and the bottom of the fraction by a number larger than one. For example, the fraction $\frac{40}{48}$ can be simplified by dividing the top and the bottom by 8 which is the lowest common denominator.

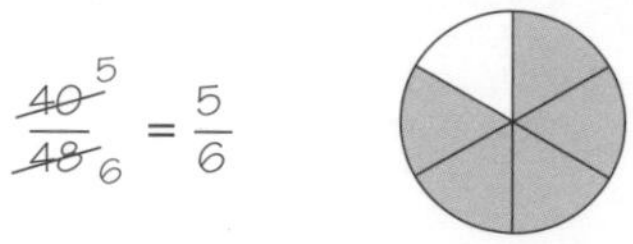

$$\frac{\cancel{40}^{5}}{\cancel{48}_{6}} = \frac{5}{6}$$

Figure 6 $\frac{5}{6}$ of a circle

The fraction $\frac{5}{6}$ is in its simplest form as no whole number, other than one, will divide exactly into both 5 and 6.

Fractions can be multiplied and added together. However, as will be demonstrated, adding fractions together is more complex than multiplying them.

When two fractions are multiplied together, the new numerator (the top half) is found by multiplying together the two numerators; and the new denominator (the bottom half) is found by multiplying the two denominators. For example, to multiply $\frac{4}{5}$ by $\frac{2}{8}$ the following steps are needed:

$$\frac{4}{5} \times \frac{2}{8} = \frac{(4 \times 2)}{(5 \times 8)} = \frac{8}{40}$$

This can be simplified to $\frac{1}{5}$ by dividing both numerator and denominator by 8.

To add fractions, each must first be converted so that they have a common denominator. So, to add $\frac{4}{5}$ to $\frac{3}{8}$, the top and bottom of the first fraction are first multiplied by the denominator of the second, so that $\frac{4}{5}$ becomes $\frac{32}{40}$ (multiply by 8). Then the top and the bottom of the second fraction are multiplied by the denominator of the first so that $\frac{3}{8}$ becomes $\frac{15}{40}$ (multiply by 5). The two fractions now have the same denominators so that they can be added together.

$$\frac{32}{40} + \frac{15}{40} = \frac{32+15}{40} = \frac{47}{40} = 1\frac{7}{40}$$

Scientific calculator: fractions

When your calculator is in Math mode, as recommended, fractions are entered by using the ▦ button in the left-hand column of the function key area of the calculator keypad. This displays a fraction 'template' on the display that contains boxes that need to be 'filled in'.

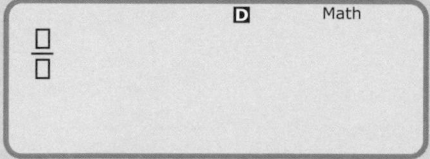

Figure 7   Calculator display in Math mode

When the button is first pressed, the cursor is located in the top box ready for you to enter the numerator. To move to the bottom box to enter the denominator, use the cursor down key ▼. If there are further parts of a calculation to be entered when the template has been completed, the right cursor key ⏵ can be used to move out of the denominator in preparation for the input of the rest of the calculation.

Mixed numbers such as $1\frac{2}{3}$ can be entered similarly using the mixed number template obtained using the key sequence (SHIFT)▦ (▭ $\frac{□}{□}$). This template provides three boxes to fill, one for the whole number part, and one each for the numerator and denominator of the fractional part.

Any fractional answers to calculations will automatically be displayed in lowest terms.

Activity 1.4 ....

Although it is often convenient to explain proportions in terms of fractions, such as indicating that one quarter of customers want their purchases delivered, in accounting it is easier to express these in decimals.

Convert the following fractions into decimals (give your answers to 3 d.p.):

(a) $\frac{1}{8}$　(b) $\frac{1}{11}$　(c) $\frac{2}{16}$　(d) $\frac{3}{16}$　(e) $\frac{5}{4}$　(f) $\frac{7}{47}$

(g) $\frac{101}{8}$　(h) $\frac{99}{100}$　(i) $\frac{2}{1,000}$　(j) $\frac{16}{4}$

Complete the following calculations:

(k) $\left(\frac{30}{6}\right) - 2$　(l) $\frac{24 \times 4}{3}$　(m) $\left(\frac{12+3}{5}\right) - 2$

(n) $69 - [4 \times (7 + 3)]$

Feedback ....

(a)　0.125　(b)　0.091　(c)　0.125　(d)　0.188
(e)　1.250　(f)　0.149　(g)　12.625　(h)　0.990
(i)　0.002　(j)　4.000

(k) $\left(\frac{30}{6}\right) - 2 = 3$ enter (▦ 30 in top square and 6 in bottom square using the arrows on the button to navigate), then – 2

(l) $\frac{24 \times 4}{3} = 32$　(m) $\left(\frac{12+3}{5}\right) - 2 = 1$　(n) $69 - [4 \times (7 + 3)] = 29$

When using a scientific calculator to answer part (a) enter $1 \div 8 =$. If the answer given is $\frac{1}{8}$ press (S↔D) to get 0.125.

You will meet fractions again in Session 4, which covers probability.

1.5 Ratios

Ratios show the relative shares of the whole. They show how something should be divided up. Ratios give the same information as fractions, although the ratio does not show the denominator. For example, assume that you cut a cake into eight slices, and give five slices to family members and three slices to friends. This would give a ratio of 5:3 in favour of your family. Expressed in fractions this would be $\frac{5}{8} : \frac{3}{8}$ (the denominator being 8 in both fractions).

Suppose that three waiters in a small café share tips according to the hours they work each day. Bill works 5 hours, Jim 8 and Ann 3. On Monday tips totalled £64. How much will each receive?

First add up the hours: $5 + 8 + 3 = 16$, so the total tip money is divided into sixteen equal parts, that is, in the ratio of 5:8:3, then give Bill five parts, Jim eight parts and Ann three parts.

> £64 ÷ 16 = £4 (i.e., each part is £4)
> Bill's share is 5 × £4 = £20
> Jim's share is 8 × £4 = £32
> Ann's share is 3 × £4 = £12

Check for correctness by adding up all the shares:
£20 + £32 + £12 = £64

The above method will work every time. Let us look at another example.

Technical Components Limited has just declared a dividend of £27,000. The company has six shareholders and the number of shares each one holds is shown in brackets after their name: John (30,000), Sally (25,000), Lee (15,000), Jeff (10,000), Mandy (8,000) and Adam (2,000). How much dividend does each shareholder receive?

> Number of parts: $30 + 25 + 15 + 10 + 8 + 2 = 90$ (Note that the last three zeros have been ignored to simplify the calculation.)
> The value of each part is £27,000 ÷ 90 = £300

			£		£
John	30	×	300	=	9,000
Sally	25	×	300	=	7,500
Lee	15	×	300	=	4,500
Jeff	10	×	300	=	3,000
Mandy	8	×	300	=	2,400
Adam	2	×	300	=	600
Check					27,000

Activity 1.5

Jacques, Chloe and Loykie are in partnership. Calculate their profit share if they share profits of €17,000 in the ratio of:

(a) 2:3:5

(b) 3:2:2

(c) 4:3:1

Feedback

(a) Number of parts: 10
　　Value of each part: €17,000 ÷ 10 = €1,700

			€		€
Jacques	2	×	1,700	=	3,400
Chloe	3	×	1,700	=	5,100
Loykie	5	×	1,700	=	8,500
Check					17,000

(b) €17,000 ÷ 7 = €2,428.57

			€		€
Jacques	3	×	2,428.57	=	7,286
Chloe	2	×	2,428.57	=	4,857
Loykie	2	×	2,428.57	=	4,857
Check					17,000

(c) €17,000 ÷ 8 = €2,125

			€		€
Jacques	4	×	€2,125	=	8,500
Chloe	3	×	€2,125	=	6,375
Loykie	1	×	€2,125	=	2,125
Check					17,000

1.6 Percentages

A **percentage** is a proportion or a rate per hundred. So 30% means 30 out of 100. For example, if a shop owner employs 14 sales assistants, 2 supervisors and 4 delivery drivers, the total number of workers adds up to 20 which is the absolute value of staff numbers. The percentage of the total employees in each category of staff is:

	Sales assistants	Supervisors	Drivers	Total value
Individual numbers	14	2	4	20
Percentages (relative values)	70%	10%	20%	100%

The percentage of staff who are sales assistants is calculated as $\frac{14}{20} \times 100 = 70\%$.

The unique feature of percentages is that they relate to a denominator of 100 and the total parts always add up to 100. So the words 'per cent' mean 'out of 100'.

Percentages can be expressed either as fractions or as decimals:

$$70\% = \frac{70}{100} \text{ or } 0.7$$

$$10\% = \frac{10}{100} \text{ or } 0.1$$

$$20\% = \frac{20}{100} \text{ or } 0.2$$

To convert a fraction into a percentage, change the fraction into a decimal and then multiply by 100:

$$\frac{9}{10} = 0.9 = 90\% \qquad \frac{9}{20} = 0.45 = 45\% \qquad \frac{2}{4} = 0.5 = 50\%$$

Percentages need to be expressed as a percentage of something.

If a business buys wine glasses at £145 per box plus 5% carriage, then the actual cost of a box of wine glasses is:

$$£145 + (5\% \text{ of } £145) = £145 + (0.05 \times £145) = £152.25$$

Alternatively, the amount can be calculated as:

$$£145 \times (100\% + 5\%) = £145 \times 1.05 = £152.25$$

If a business makes 20% profit on all sales of tables and it sells £45,000 worth of tables during the year (i.e., £45,000 includes 20% profit), then the actual cost of tables is:

$$£45,000 \times \frac{100}{120} = £37,500 \quad \text{or} \quad \frac{£45,000}{1.20} = £37,500$$

If a company pays a 5% dividend on its 150,000 £1 ordinary shares, the total dividend payable is £150,000 × 5% = £7,500.

Activity 1.6

Joe increases the price of model N5 refrigerators by 15%. The new selling price is £275. What was the price before the increase came into effect?

Feedback

	%
N5 refrigerator original	100
Increase	15
N5 refrigerator after increase	115

The price after the increase was £275.

Therefore 115% of the original price = £275.

So the original price was $\frac{100}{115} \times £275 = £239.13$.

This amount was probably rounded to £239.

Activity 1.7

It is useful to be able to compare information shown in differing formats, for example, a ready-reckoner table converting pints to litres. The following table of equivalences is incomplete. Complete it by converting each figure shown into its equivalent decimal, fraction or percentage.

Percentage	Decimal	Fraction
1%		
	0.04	
		$\frac{1}{10}$
$12\frac{1}{2}\%$		
	0.25	
		$\frac{1}{3}$
	0.5	
		$\frac{19}{20}$

Feedback

Percentage	Decimal	Fraction
1%	0.01	$\frac{1}{100}$
4%	0.04	$\frac{1}{25}$
10%	0.1	$\frac{1}{10}$
$12\frac{1}{2}$%	0.125	$\frac{1}{8}$
25%	0.25	$\frac{1}{4}$
33.33%	0.3333	$\frac{1}{3}$
50%	0.5	$\frac{1}{2}$
95%	0.95	$\frac{19}{20}$

1.7 Negative numbers

Numbers smaller than zero are called negative numbers. Most people have no problems adding positive numbers together and subtracting positive numbers from each other. However, when it comes to dealing with negative numbers some people experience difficulties.

Both positive and negative numbers can be represented by a number line.

Figure 8 A number line

In the middle is the number zero, positive numbers are shown to the right and negative numbers to the left.

For a simple sum 2 + 3 = 5, the calculation can be checked using the number line. Find 2 on the number line and move three places *to the right* to give 5.

Now look at the sum –2 + –4. Find –2 on the number line and move 4 places this time *to the left*; this gives –6.

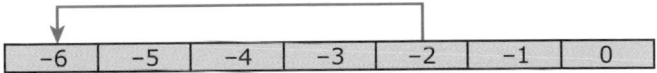

Figure 9 Using the number line to check a simple sum

The number line can be used for more complicated calculations by drawing part of the line. Consider the sum –3 + 8 – –6. This is often expressed as –3 + 8 – (–6). Find –3 on the number line; add the positive number (so move to the right) to get +5.

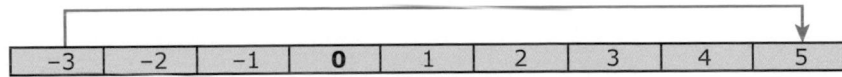

Figure 10 Using the number line to check a more complicated calculation

Then move 6 places to the right to get +11.

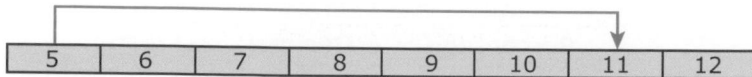

Figure 11   Using the number line to check a more complicated calculation

Of course, you could just learn the following rules for dealing with negative numbers. However using a number line can aid understanding and once you have practised a few calculations using a number line, dealing with negative numbers will become much easier.

Addition and subtraction

- Adding a negative number is the same as subtracting a positive one
- Subtracting a negative number is the same as adding a positive one

There are also rules for multiplication and division, as below.

Multiplication and division

Where the signs are different, the answer is negative (i.e., a plus and a minus equals a minus).
- A positive number multiplied by a negative number gives a negative (i.e., a plus times a minus equals a minus), so + × – gives –
- A positive number divided by a negative number gives a negative (i.e., a plus divided by a minus equals a minus), so + ÷ – gives –

Where the signs are the same, the answer is positive (i.e., two pluses or two minuses equals a plus)
- A negative number multiplied by a negative number gives a positive (i.e., a minus times a minus equals a plus), so – × – gives +
- A negative number divided by a negative number gives a positive (i.e., a minus divided by a minus equals a plus), so – ÷ – gives +

Once you understand the theory of dealing with negative numbers, you should move on to manipulating negative numbers using your calculator. However it will be important that you enter figures correctly. Many calculators have a change of sign button: +/– the scientific calculator does not have such a key, you will need to use the ◀ and delete key and replace the sign.

Minus 6 should be displayed on your calculator as –6 or 6–. The +/– button is used to turn a positive number into a negative one and vice versa. Remember to always enter the number first and then change the sign.

Scientific calculator: using your calculator for negative numbers

There are two different mathematical uses for the minus sign (–):
- As the symbol for subtraction, as in 5 – 3
- To indicate a negative number such as –2.

Corresponding to these there are two different minus sign keys on the calculator:
- –, which is used for the operation of subtraction, as in **5 – 3**
- **(–)**, which is used for negative numbers, e.g., **(–) 2**.

In fact, the Casio fx-83ES and related models permit the – key to be used for both purposes, but many other calculators require the equivalent of the **(–)** key to be used for negative numbers.

Note that if you attempt to use **(–)** for subtraction, for example, **3(–)2**, you will generate a syntax error.

Activity 1.8 ....

Try the following sums using first a number line (or part of one) and then using the rule above, before finally using your calculator.

(a)   4 × −8 =

(b)   10 ÷ −5 =

(c)   −5 × −8 =

(d) −12 ÷ −3 =

(e) 3 + 3 − 3 =

(f) −8 − 3 − 7 =

(g) −15 ÷ −3 =

(h)   −7 × −5 =

Feedback ....

(a)   4 × −8 = −32

(b)   10 ÷ −5 = −2

(c)   −5 × −8 = 40

(d) −12 ÷ −3 =   4

(e) 3 + 3 − 3 =   3

(f) −8 − 3 − 7 = −18

(g) −15 ÷ −3 =   5

(h)   −7 × −5 = 35

1.8 Tests of reasonableness

When using a calculator or computer to carry out a calculation, it is important that you have some idea as to whether the answer looks reasonable or whether you could have pressed a wrong key.

If you use a calculator to add 48 to 39 and arrive at an answer of 107, you should know immediately that there is a mistake somewhere, as two numbers under 50 can never total more than 100.

Another way to test for reasonableness is to round numbers. For example, if you are adding 2,496 to 5,728 you could round these numbers to 2,500 and 5,700 so the answer you should expect from your calculator should be in the region of 8,200.

Activity 1.9 ....

Choose the correct answer purely on what appears to be most reasonable. Do not use a calculator, or calculate the answer mentally but rather try to develop a rough estimate for what the answer should be. Then determine from the choices presented to you which makes the most sense, that is, the most reasonable.

(a) 126 ÷ 7 =

   (1) 180

   (2) 0.18

   (3) 18

   (4) 1.8

(b) 17 × 26 =

   (1) 44.2

   (2) 442

   (3) 4,420

   (4) 44,200

(c) 6,460 / 760 =
   (1) 850
   (2) 0.85
   (3) 8.5
   (4) 85

(d) 330 × 8.4 =
   (1) 277.2
   (2) 2,772
   (3) 27,772

(e) 269 + 378 =
   (1) 547
   (2) 747
   (3) 647

(f) 562 − 268 =
   (1) 194
   (2) 294
   (3) 394

Feedback

(a) (3): 18
(b) (2): 442
(c) (3): 8.5
(d) (2): 2,772
(e) (3): 647
(f) (2): 294

1.9 Powers and roots

1.9.1   Powers

Raising a number to a 'power' means multiplying the number by itself a specific number of times. For example, x^2 (known as x squared) is the shorthand for $x \times x$; x^3 (known as x cubed) is the shorthand for $x \times x \times x$; and x^n is the shorthand for x multiplied by itself n times.

$$6^2 = 6 \times 6 = 36$$

$$6^3 = 6 \times 6 \times 6 = 216$$

Scientific calculator: powers

For small powers such as squares or cubes there are dedicated buttons, x^2 and x^3, which are located in the function key area of the keypad. These are used in a similar manner to how you would write mathematics. For example, to enter 3^2 you would press ⒊ $\boxed{x^2}$. The display also shows the maths in the same way as you would write it on paper.

To calculate higher powers, for example, 2^5, you need to use the more general power key $\boxed{x^\blacksquare}$. This is again used in a natural way. To enter 2^5, you use the key sequence ⒉ $\boxed{x^\blacksquare}$ ⒌. Note that after you press the $\boxed{x^\blacksquare}$ key, a small box is shown on the calculator display containing the flashing cursor ('|'), which enables you to enter the power in the correct place. To move the cursor away from this box and back to the main line of the display once the power has been entered, press the right arrow key ⊳ on the cursor control button.

1.9.2 Roots

A **root** is the opposite of a power. The **square root** ($\sqrt{\ }$) is the number or quantity which, when multiplied by itself, produces the number of which it is the square root. For example, 3 is the square root of 9, that is, $\sqrt{9} = 3$ (as $3 \times 3 = 9$).

A **cube root** ($\sqrt[3]{\ }$) of a number is the value which, when multiplied by itself twice, equals the original number. For example, $\sqrt[3]{8} = \sqrt[3]{2 \times 2 \times 2} = 2$.

Scientific calculator: roots

Just as there are keys on your calculator for entering powers, roots can also be entered directly. Square roots can be calculated using the $\boxed{\sqrt{\blacksquare}}$ key. For example, $\sqrt{2}$ can be entered using $\boxed{\sqrt{\blacksquare}}\,\boxed{2}$. Cube roots are entered using the second function of this key. For higher roots, such as fourth or fifth roots you need to use the more general ($\sqrt[\square]{\square}$) template, which is the second function of the $\boxed{x^{\blacksquare}}$ (SHIFT $\boxed{x^{\blacksquare}}$) key. This template is filled in by using the number and arrow keys $\boxed{\blacktriangleleft}$ and $\boxed{\blacktriangleright}$ in a way similar to that used when the fraction template is completed.

Calculator activity

Take a few minutes to practise using the square root button on your calculator.

1.9.3 Using powers and roots

When dealing with powers and roots there are certain rules that need to be followed.

In multiplying: add powers

When a number with a power is multiplied by the *same number* (5 in the example below) with the same or different power, *add* the powers.

For example:

$$5^2 \times 5^4 = (5 \times 5) \times (5 \times 5 \times 5 \times 5) = 5^6 = 15{,}625 \quad \text{or}$$

$$5^2 \times 5^4 = 5^{(2+4)} = 5^6 = 15{,}625$$

In division: subtract powers

When a number with a power is divided by the *same number* (8 in the example below) with the same or different power, *subtract* one power from the other.

For example:

$$8^5 \div 8^3 = 8^{(5-3)} = 8^2 = 64$$

$$3^4 \div 3^2 = 3^{(4-2)} = 3^2 = 9$$

Raising to the power: multiply indices

When a number to a power is raised to a power, the powers are multiplied.

For example:

The logic here is: 3^2 gives (3×3) and you do this three times.

$$(3^2)^3 = (3 \times 3) \times (3 \times 3) \times (3 \times 3) = 729$$

or

$$(3^2)^3 = 3^{(2 \times 3)} = 3^6 = 729$$

Roots of powers: divide indices

To find the square root of a power, divide the power by two.
For example, the square root of 3^6 is 3 to the power 6 divided by 2 ($3^{6 \div 2}$, which is 3^3). For the cube root of a power, divide it by three.

A number to the power of 1 equals that number

Any number to the power of one equals that number.

$$10^1 = 10$$

$$8^4 \div 8^3 = 8^{(4-3)} = 8^1 = 8, \text{i.e.,} \quad \frac{8 \times 8 \times 8 \times 8}{8 \times 8 \times 8}.$$

Anything to the power of 0 is 1

Any number to the power of zero equals one.

$$10^0 = 1$$
$$10^5 \div 10^5 = 10^{(5-5)} = 10^0 = 1 \text{ as any number divided}$$
by itself equals 1.

1 to any power is 1

One to any power equals one

$$1^1 = 1 \ (1 = 1)$$

$$1^2 = 1 \ (1 \times 1 = 1)$$

$$1^3 = 1 \ (1 \times 1 \times 1 = 1)$$

A power can be a fraction

A power that is expressed as a fraction can also be expressed as a root.

$$x^{\frac{1}{2}} = \sqrt{x} \text{ (the square root of } x)$$

$$4^{\frac{1}{2}} = \sqrt{4} = 2$$

$$10^{\frac{2}{3}} = \sqrt[3]{10^2}$$

$$8^{\frac{1}{3}} = \sqrt[3]{8}$$

A power can be a negative

$$10^{-2} = \frac{1}{10^2}$$

$$10^{-3} = \frac{1}{10^3} = \frac{1}{1,000}$$

A fraction can be written out in full and then simplified by cancelling, where possible, each common numerator and denominator.

$$8^5 \div 8^7 = \frac{8 \times 8 \times 8 \times 8 \times 8}{8 \times 8 \times 8 \times 8 \times 8 \times 8 \times 8} = \frac{1}{8^2}$$

and $8^5 \div 8^7 = 8^{-2} = \frac{1}{8^2}$

Now complete the following activity.

Activity 1.10 ....

(a) Use your scientific calculator to calculate the following powers:

  (1) 9^9

  (2) 10^{-4}

  (3) $16^{\frac{1}{2}}$

  (4) $8^{2.5}$

  (5) $3^{0.5}$

  (6) 6^6

  (7) $21^{-0.6}$

  (8) 1^6

  (9) 12^4

  (10) 12^0

(b) Calculate each of the following roots, giving your answer correct to 3 s.f. (significant figures).

  (1) $\sqrt{1,246}$

  (2) $\sqrt[3]{43}$

  (3) $\sqrt[5]{236}$

  (4) $\sqrt{426}$

Feedback ....

(a) Powers

  (1) $9^9 = 387,420,489$; enter 9 $\boxed{x^\blacksquare}$ 9 =

  (2) $10^{-4} = \dfrac{1}{10,000} = 0.0001$; enter 10 $\boxed{x^\blacksquare}$ – 4 =

  (3) $16^{\frac{1}{2}} = 4$; enter 16 $\boxed{x^\blacksquare}$ $\boxed{\blacksquare}$ 1 $\bigcirc\!\!\!\downarrow$ 2 =

  (4) $8^{2.5} = 181.0193$; enter 8 $\boxed{x^\blacksquare}$ 2.5 =

  (5) $3^{0.5} = 3^{\frac{1}{2}} = \sqrt{3} - 1.732$

  (6) $6^6 = 46,656$; enter 6 $\boxed{x^\blacksquare}$ 6 =

  (7) $21^{-0.6} = 0.1609$; enter 21 $\boxed{x^\blacksquare}$ – 0.6 =

  (8) $1^6 = 1$

  (9) $12^4 = 20,736$

  (10) $12^0 = 1$

(b) Roots. Answers are given to 3 s.f.

  (1) $\sqrt{1,246} = 35.3$: enter $\boxed{\sqrt{\blacksquare}}$ then 1,246

  (2) $\sqrt[3]{43} = 3.50$: enter SHIFT $\boxed{x^\blacksquare}$ (which will show $\boxed{\sqrt[\blacksquare]{\blacksquare}}$) enter 3 $\blacktriangleright$ 43 =

  (3) $\sqrt[5]{236} = 2.98$: enter SHIFT $\boxed{x^\blacksquare}$ 5 $\blacktriangleright$ 236 =

  (4) $\sqrt{426} = 20.6$: enter $\boxed{\sqrt{\blacksquare}}$ 426 = then use $\boxed{S\text{-}D}$ = to obtain the decimal

1.10 Simple equations

Up to this point in your studies, all the problems have been expressed using specific numbers. However, symbols can be used to stand for any numbers. When something can assume different numerical values, it is called a **variable**.

Variables are often designated by a symbol. These symbols can be treated as though they were numbers that are not known, and can be worked out using rules of simple equations, as will be explained.

The symbols for numbers that are most commonly used are the lower case letters of the alphabet, a, b, c, x, y, z (some of which have stylised mathematical forms or are often italicised), but occasionally letters of the Greek alphabet are used as well. Please be careful not to mix the symbol x (to represent a number) with the symbol $\times$ (to denote multiplication).

Take the following simple equation: it is a simple equation because it contains only one unknown variable:

$$4x + 7 = 19$$

To solve an equation, it needs to be manipulated so that x (the unknown variable) appears on the left-hand side and the numbers appear on the right-hand side, namely:

unknown variable = something with just numbers in

The rule is that you can do anything to one side as long as you do the same to the other side. The two sides are equal and they will stay equal as long as you do the same to each side.

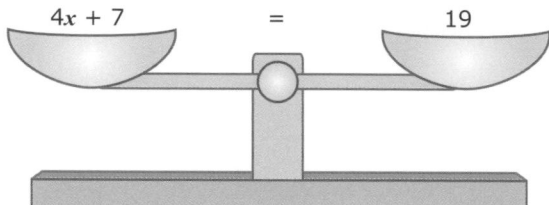

Figure 12   Scales showing how one side of an equation is equal to the other side

To solve the equation, the x needs to be on one side and the numbers on the other.

Step 1   Subtract 7 from each side. This gives $4x = 12$.

Step 2   Divide each side by 4. This gives $x = 3$.

Let us solve some more equations!

(a) £284 = £564 – c

Adding c to each side gives £284 + c = £564

Subtracting £284 from each side gives c = £280.

(b) $5y + 11 = 8y - 4$

Adding 4 to each side gives $5y + 15 = 8y$

Subtracting $5y$ from each side gives $15 = 3y$

Dividing each side by 3 gives $y = 5$.

(c) $6\sqrt{x} + 28 = 65.4$

Subtracting 28 from each side gives $6\sqrt{x} = 37.4$

Dividing each side by 6 gives $\sqrt{x} = 6.233$

Squaring each side gives $x = 38.850$.

(d) $y = \sqrt{6x + 4}$

Squaring each side gives $y^2 = 6x + 4$

Subtracting 4 from each side gives $y^2 - 4 = 6x$

Dividing each side by 6 gives $x = \dfrac{y^2 - 4}{6}$

Note: this solution does not provide an absolute value of x because the value of x depends on the value of y.

(e) Simplify $4(x + 7y - 2)$

Multiply each of the numbers inside the brackets by the number outside the brackets to give $4x + 28y - 8$. Nothing else can be done.

Activity 1.11

Before moving on to simultaneous equations in Section 1.11, please complete this activity.

Find the value of x or y in each of the following equations:

(a) $10x + 5 = 25$

(b) $20y + 78 = 33y - 26$

(c) $4\sqrt{x} + 17 = 65.1$

(d) $28x + 2{,}210 = 45x$

Feedback

Equation	Solution
(a) $10x + 5 = 25$	$10x = 20$, so $x = 2$.
(b) $20y + 78 = 33y - 26$	Add 26 to each side: $20y + 104 = 33y$
	Subtract $20y$ from each side: $104 = 13y$
	Divide each side by 13: $y = 8$.
(c) $4\sqrt{x} + 17 = 65.4$	Subtract 17 from each side: $4\sqrt{x} = 48.4$
	Divide each side by 4: $\sqrt{x} = 12.1$
	Square each side: $x = 146.41$.
(d) $28x + 2{,}210 = 45x$	Subtract $28x$ from each side: $2{,}210 = 17x$
	Divide $2{,}210$ by 17 to get $x = 130$.

1.11 Simultaneous equations

When a single equation contains two unknowns, that is, x and y, it is not possible to find either x or y. For example, the equation $x + y = 6$ has a whole range of values for x and y such as $x - 1$ and $y = 5$; $x = 2$ and $y = 4$; $x = 3$ and $y = 3$; $x = 4$ and $y = 2$; $x = 5$ and $y = 1$; $x = 10$ and $y = -4$, and so on.

If there are two equations each containing x and y, then there is only one value for x and one for y that satisfies both equations. Such pairs of equations are called **simultaneous equations.** The method for solving simultaneous equations (i.e., to work out what is x and y) is straightforward, although the arithmetic can be tedious if carried out manually. Using a scientific calculator will help with this problem.

Consider the following pair of equations:

$$2x + 6y = 16 \quad \text{(equation 1)}$$

$$x + 2y - 4 \quad \text{(equation 2)}$$

To find x and y from this pair of equations, four steps are needed.

Step 1 Change equation 2 so that it has the same number of x as equation 1 by multiplying both sides of equation 2 by 2. This gives equation 3:

$$x + 2y = 4 \quad \text{(equation 2)}$$

$$2x + 4y = 8 \quad \text{(equation 3)}$$

Step 2   Subtract equation 3 from equation 1

$$2x + 6y = 16 \quad \text{(equation 1)}$$

$$2x + 4y = 8 \quad \text{(equation 3)}$$

$$2y = 8$$

This eliminates x and therefore $y = 4$.

Step 3   To find x, substitute 4 for y into equation 2:

$$x + 2y = 4 \quad \text{(equation 2)}$$

This becomes $x + 8 = 4$, so $x = 4 - 8$ and $x = -4$.

Step 4   Check equation 1 by using $y = 4$ and $x = -4$:

$2x + 6y = 16$ becomes $(2 \times -4) + (6 \times 4) = 16$, so $-8 + 24 = 16$ which is correct.

'I think you should be more explicit in step 2.'

Simultaneous equations will be used in regression analysis later in the module, so try solving the equations in Activity 1.12.

Activity 1.12 ....

Solve the following simultaneous equations:

$$745 = 15a + 40b \quad \text{(equation 1)}$$

$$1,840 = 45a + 340b \quad \text{(equation 2)}$$

Feedback ....

$a = 54.453$ and $b = -1.795$

To solve the simultaneous equations:

Multiply equation 1 by 3, as $3 \times 15 = 45$ so both values of a become the same.

$$2,235 = 45a + 120b$$
$$1,840 = 45a + 340b$$

Then deduct one equation from the other:

$$2,235 = 45a + 120b$$
$$1,840 = 45a + 340b$$
$$395 = -220b$$

Then divide 395 by 220 to find the value of *b*. Therefore *b* = −1.795.

Putting *b* = −1.795 into equation 1 gives 745 = 15*a* + −1.795(40).

Multiply −1.795 by 40, so the equation then becomes 745 = 15*a* + −71.8.

Add 71.8 to both sides to get rid of the −71.8; this gives 816.8 = 15*a*.

Divide 816.8 by 15 to find the value of *a*. Therefore *a* = 54.453.

Summary

This session was designed to prepare you for later sessions in this and other units. Some students will have found the material demanding while for others it will be a reminder of material studied in the past.

The session has covered some basic numerical skills required in accounting, from multiplication and division, through to fractions, ratios, percentages, negative numbers, powers and roots and the use of algebra in formulating and solving equations. Throughout the session you were shown how calculations can be performed using a scientific calculator, as this may be your first experience of using such a calculator.

Session 2 goes on to introduce some quantitative methods for summarising and analysing data.

SESSION **2 Summarising, presenting an** **analysing data**

Introduction

Upon completion of Session 2, you are expected to be able to:

- use tables to summarise and present data
- use bar charts, line graphs, time series graphs, pie charts and scatter graphs to present tabulated data
- construct an appropriate chart based on a typical management accounting statement
- understand and use frequency distributions to summarise data
- use histograms to represent frequency distributions
- understand and use measures of centrality, including mean, median and mode, to represent data
- understand and use measures of dispersion, including range, standard deviation, variance, and coefficient of variation, to represent data.

This session introduces the common quantitative methods for summarising, presenting and analysing data used by management accountants. The role of the management accountant includes clearly presenting useful information that can be used in decision making. In doing so, the accountant should be aware of the implications of risk and uncertainty. The concepts of averages, spread, and linear regression underpin risk management. Risk and uncertainty will be discussed in Session 4 of this unit.

2.1 Tables

The average manager will not have the time or the inclination to wade through raw, unorganised data, that is, data (facts) arising from an original investigation, but will require them to be presented in such a way that they will become significant and more memorable (information). Data plus meaning equal information.

The most convenient way to present data is in a table. The layout of the table will depend on the information to be presented. The table below shows a company's sales figures, by product, for six months of trading. (Several of the graphs shown in Section 2.2 are prepared using the data in this table.)

Analysis of sales

Month	Product A	Product B	Product C	Total
	£	£	£	£
1	25,000	13,500	11,500	50,000
2	27,500	14,250	24,250	66,000
3	24,500	10,450	10,050	45,000
4	51,750	22,500	20,750	95,000
5	30,000	25,000	20,000	75,000
6	31,500	21,500	13,000	66,000
Total	190,250	107,200	99,550	397,000

When drawing up a table you should ensure that:

- it has a title
- columns and rows are clearly labelled
- the nature of the data should be shown, for example, £ or units
- where appropriate, columns are totalled downwards
- where appropriate, rows are totalled on the right-hand side of the table
- where appropriate, columns and rows are by order of importance
- it is not over-cluttered so that it is easy to read: non-essential information should not be shown
- the source of the information used to draw up the table is stated. (Note that no source has been given here, because the figures were created purely for illustrative purposes.)

2.2 Charts and graphs

Charts and graphs enable data to be presented visually.

A chart is a diagrammatic representation of data whereas graphs show the relationship between two variable quantities each measured along a pair of axes, for example, how weight varies with height or how data change over time.

2.2.1 Bar charts

In its simplest form a **bar chart** consists of a number of separate bars of varying height or length, each bar representing different categories of data. A suitable scale should be chosen, and the scale should normally start at zero.

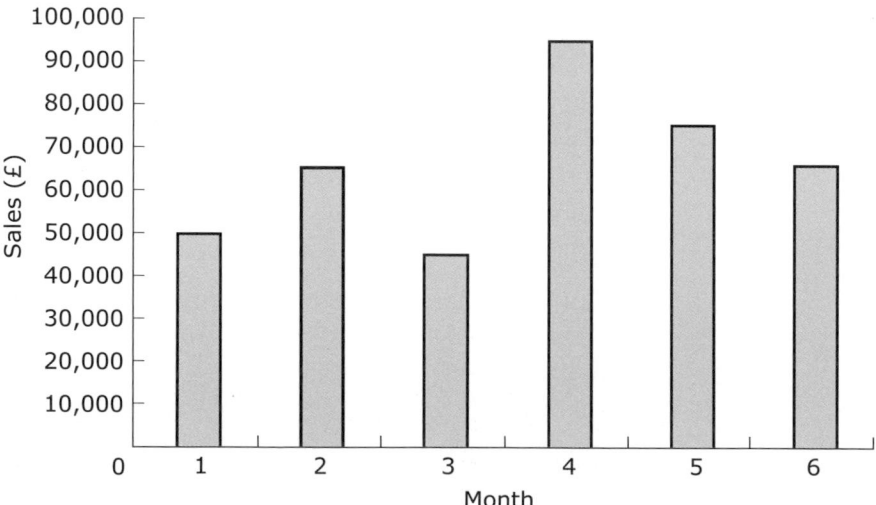

Figure 13   Bar chart: sales per month

You may also have seen a more complicated type of bar chart known as a component or stacked bar chart. This type of bar chart allows an extra dimension of the data to be shown. For example, the following component bar chart shows the total sales split between different products.

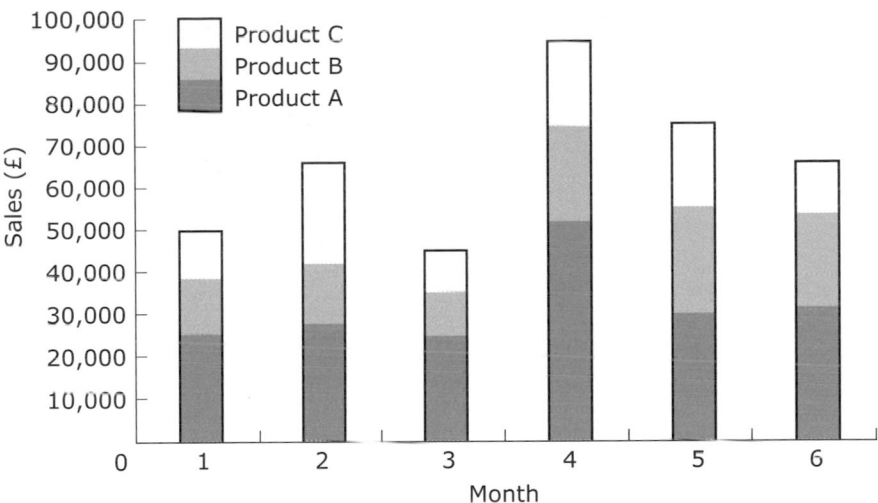

Figure 14 Component bar chart: sales per month for products A, B and C

2.2.2 Line graphs

There may be a fixed relationship between two variables, for example, the total sales price is related to the number of units purchased. If you purchase three kilos of potatoes, the total cost depends on the price per kilo. In an example of a telephone bill, the costs may be a fixed quarterly charge plus a charge per number of calls made. These relationships can be represented by the formula for a straight line:

$$y = a + bx$$

where

x is the **independent variable** (represented by the horizontal axis on a graph)

y is the **dependent variable**, that is, it is dependent on x (represented by the vertical axis on a graph)

a and b are constants.

a represents the intercept of the line on the vertical axis; a is the value of y when x equals zero.

b represents the slope of the line (the ratio of the vertical increase in y to the horizontal increase in x). Hence b is the amount by which y changes when x increases by 1.

For example, if the cost of your telephone land line comprises a fixed rental charge of £30 per quarter and a charge of 15 pence per minute for calls, your quarterly telephone bill will be calculated as follows:

Cost = £30 + 0.15x (where x is the total number
of minutes of calls made)

Putting these data into the equation of a straight line, $y = a + bx$ gives:

$$y = 30 + 0.15x$$

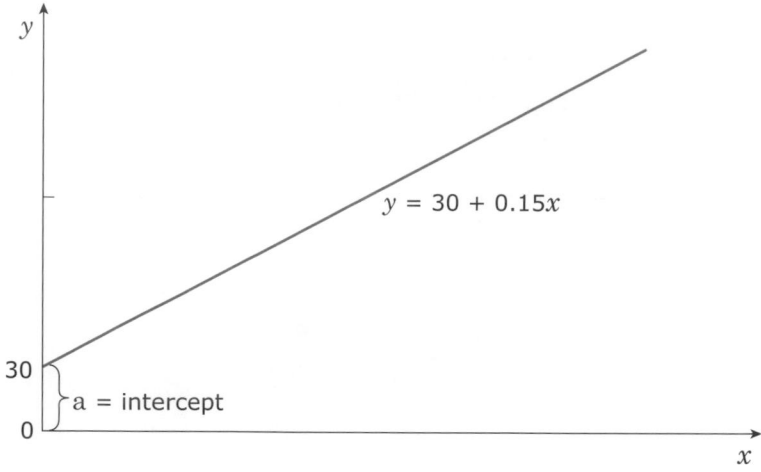

Figure 15   Straight-line graph

If two values of x are chosen and substituted into the formula, the value of y can be calculated and the points plotted on a graph.

At $x = 1,000$, $y = 30 + 0.15(1,000) = 180$

At $x = 4,000$, $y = 30 + 0.15(4,000) = 630$

If the telephone land line bills for a number of quarters are plotted on a graph, it will look something like the figure below. It is usual to plot a number of observations rather than just two.

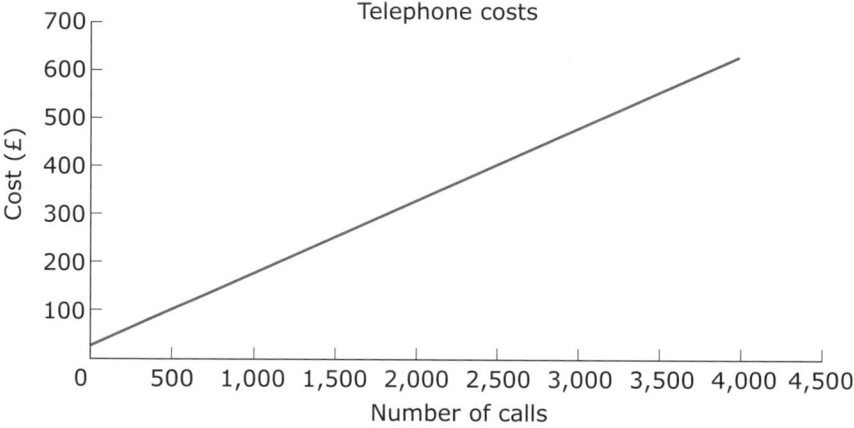

Figure 16   Straight-line graph: telephone costs per quarter

You will meet the formula of a straight line again in Section 3.5 which deals with regression analysis.

2.2.3   Time series graphs

A **time series graph** is a line graph that has time as the horizontal axis and illustrates the development of a chosen variable over time. They are used to help identify patterns and trends in data. As these graphs show how a variable has behaved in the past, they are often used to try to predict how the variable will perform in the future by identifying the underlying trends (this will be looked at in Session 3).

To draw a time series graph, the data values are plotted as points and then these points are joined up to form a continuous line. If more than one line is shown on the same axis, this is called a multiple line graph.

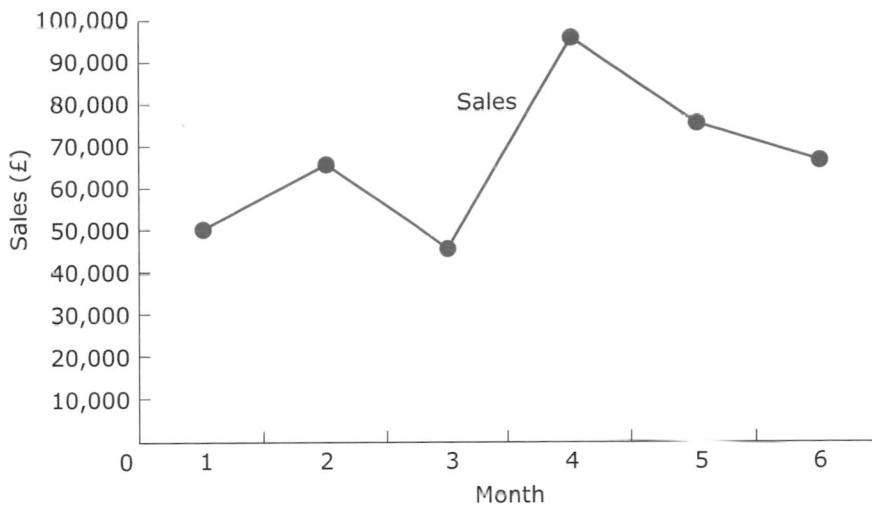

Figure 17   Time series graph

2.2.4   Pie charts

A **pie chart**, as its name implies, looks like a pie divided into slices, the pie representing the whole and the slices representing particular components.

Suppose that the staff of an organisation comprises the following:

The composition of the staff in an organisation

Role	%
Senior managers	10
Other managers	15
Administrative	35
Clerical	40
Total	100

You could show the pie chart like this:

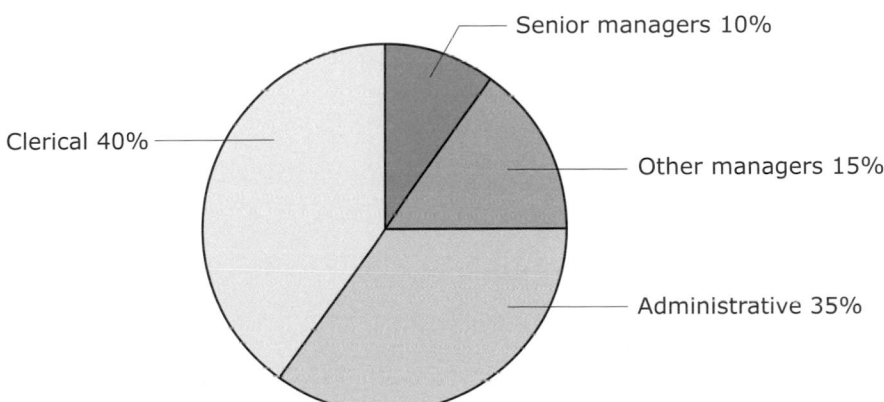

Figure 18   Pie chart: staff

The area of a segment (a slice) of the pie chart corresponds to the proportion that the category occupies in the whole. For instance, the segment marked 'Other managers' occupies 15 per cent of the whole pie.

In general, you can use a pie chart when you want to show the components of something. It is possible to use a pie chart to illustrate the composition of staff in the organisation because the data described the whole organisation. Note that the percentages sum to 100.

If the previous example had comparative figures, two pie charts could be drawn, one for each year, and the results compared visually.

2.2.5 Scatter graphs

A **scatter graph** is a graph that plots two different sets of data against one another. It is used where it is suspected that there may be a connection between the two sets of data. This area of **statistics**, which is called **correlation**, tries to establish whether there is such a connection or not. For example, a manufacturing company would expect electricity costs to move in line with output, or a company selling battery-operated toys and batteries might expect an increase in the sales of batteries to follow an increase in battery-operated toys. This is covered in more detail in Session 3.

The graph below shows the relationship between two complementary products:

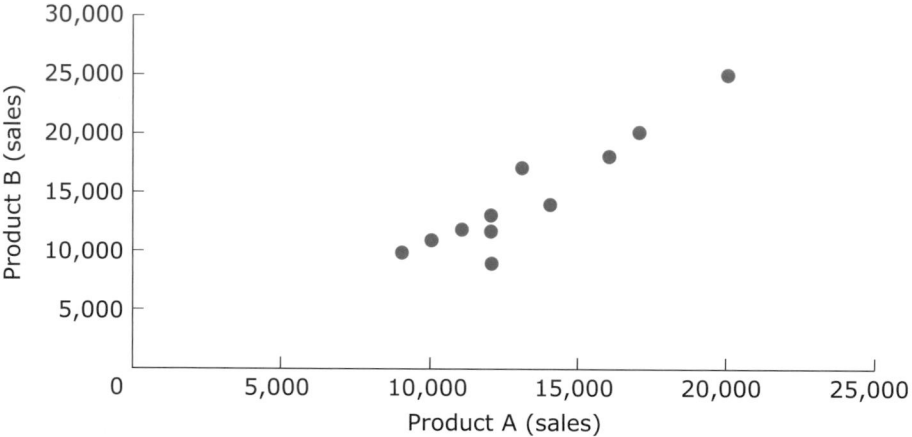

Figure 19   Scatter graph showing a relationship between variables

A company selling diverse products would not expect a relationship between them.

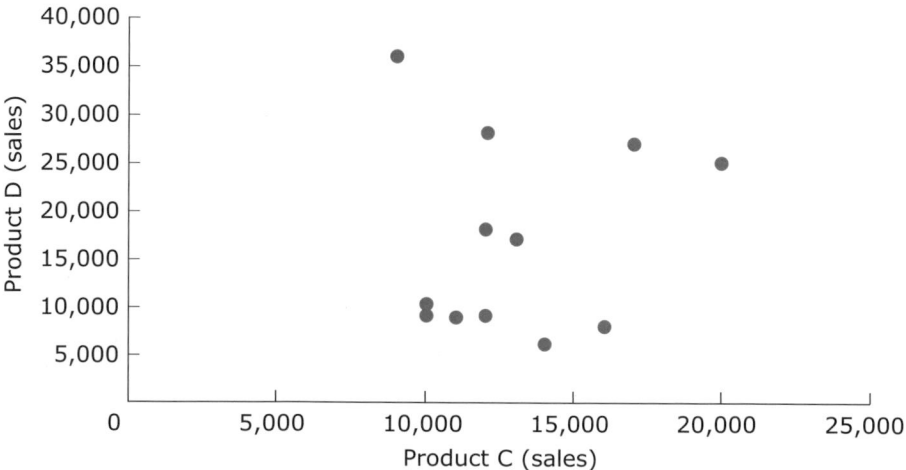

Figure 20   Scatter graph showing that there is no relationship between variables

Note that there is no attempt to connect the points representing the variables.

In constructing scatter graphs, the scale for the dependent variable should lie on the vertical axis (referred to as the *y* axis), while the scale for the independent variable should lie on the horizontal axis (referred to as the *x* axis). The reason for this is to represent the assumed cause and effect. An increase in advertising spend (the independent variable) causes sales (the dependent variable) to increase. The dependent and independent variables are discussed again in Session 3.

Activity 2.1   ....

Connect your computer to the Internet and search for the website of the Office of National Statistics. Look at some real life examples of charts and graphs.

Categories on the site which you might like to look at include:

(a) average weekly earnings

(b) population ageing

(c) family spending

(d) marriages

(e) work and worklessness.

Spend about 20 minutes on this.

Feedback   ....

The website http://www.statistics.gov.uk uses a variety of charts and graphs:

(a) average weekly earnings – line graph

(b) population ageing – component bar chart

(c) family spending – sideways bar chart

(d) marriages – complex line graph

(e) work and worklessness – bar chart with positive and negative results shown.

2.3 Constructing charts and graphs using a spreadsheet

The spreadsheet program called Excel has a Chart Wizard (on the standard toolbar) which makes creating charts easy once you have input the data. This section looks at how to construct an appropriate chart based on a typical management accounting problem. The examples show how to create a pie chart and a bar chart. Having worked through this section, you should also be able to produce line charts and time series graphs in a similar way.

2.3.1 Producing a pie chart

Before you work through the following steps, please ensure that the spreadsheet formula bar is visible (see Figure 21).

Step 1   Enter your data as shown below.

	A	B	C	D	E
1	**Spindle Motors Ltd**				
2	*Sales analysis*				
3		20X1	20X2	20X3	
4		£	£	£	
5	Product A	200,000	210,000	215,000	
6	Product B	140,000	146,000	148,000	
7	Product C	52,000	55,000	57,000	
8	Product D	46,000	47,000	49,000	
9	Total sales	438,000	458,000	469,000	
10					

Highlight the data you wish to appear in the chart. In this case to produce a pie chart showing the 20X1 figures, highlight cells down from A5 to A8 and then move the mouse pointer across to highlight cells B5 to B8.

Click on the chart icon on the spreadsheet toolbar: it looks like a pie chart.

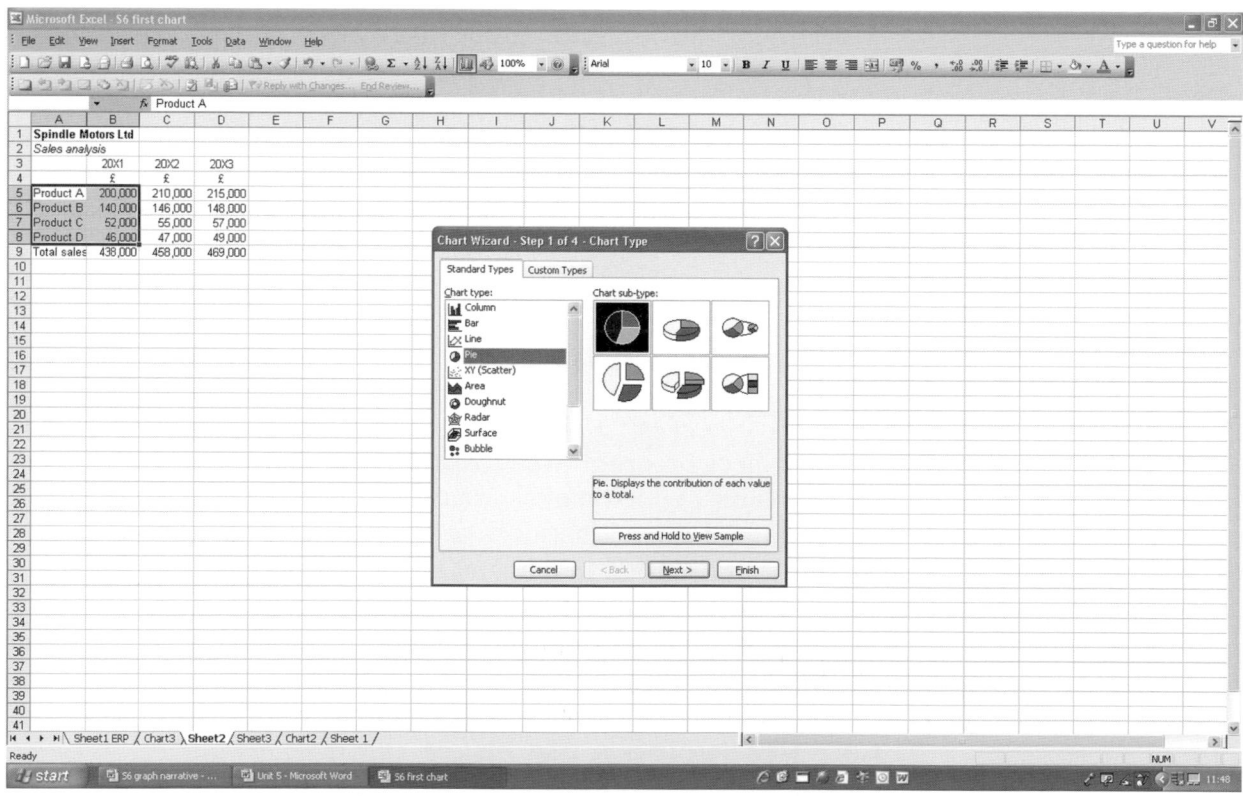

Figure 21   Spreadsheet showing Chart Wizard – Step 1 of 4 – Chart Type

Choose the chart type pie.

Step 2   Click Next and accept the data range given; then click Next.

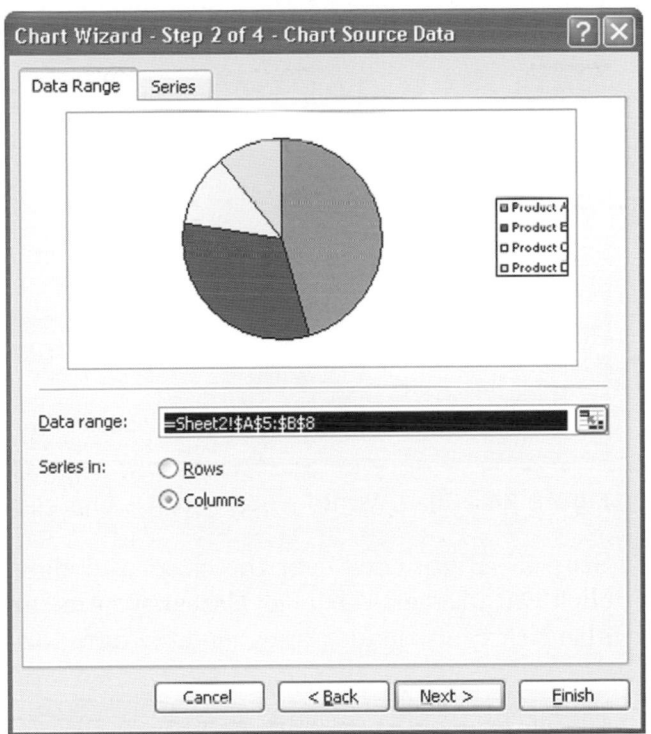

Figure 22   Chart Wizard – Step 2 of 4 – Chart Source Data (Data Range)

Step 3   Enter the chart title 'Sales analysis'.

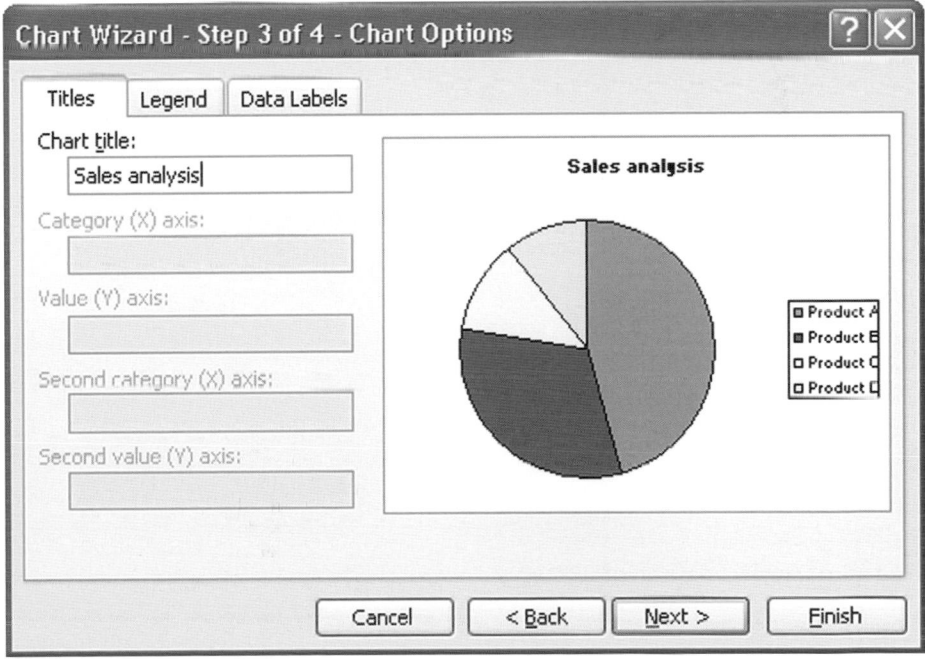

Figure 23   Chart Wizard – Step 3 of 4 – Chart Options (Titles)

Step 4   The next screen (Chart Location) allows you to choose whether you want the chart to appear on the current worksheet along with the data or on a separate sheet. Make your choice and then click Finish. The Chart Location given was accepted. Click Finish.

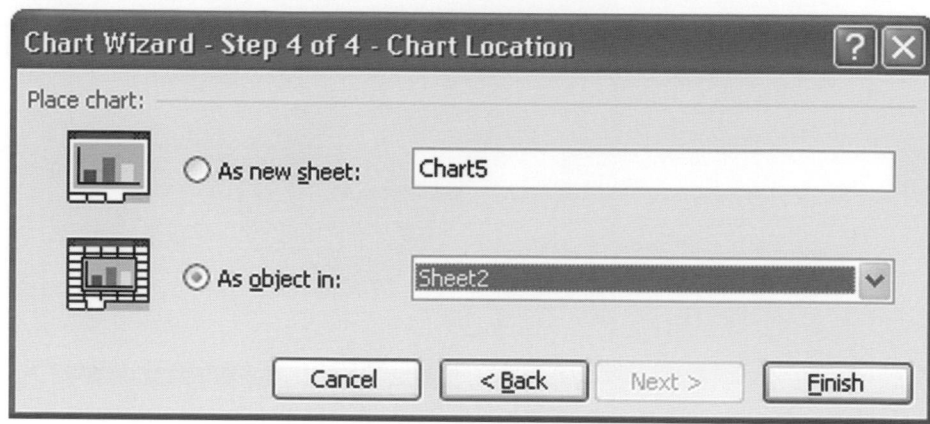

Figure 24   Chart Wizard – Step 4 of 4 – Chart Location

Step 5   Right click over the chart and choose Format Data Series, click Data Labels tab, click Category name and Percentage (you could also tick Show leader lines as done here) and click OK.

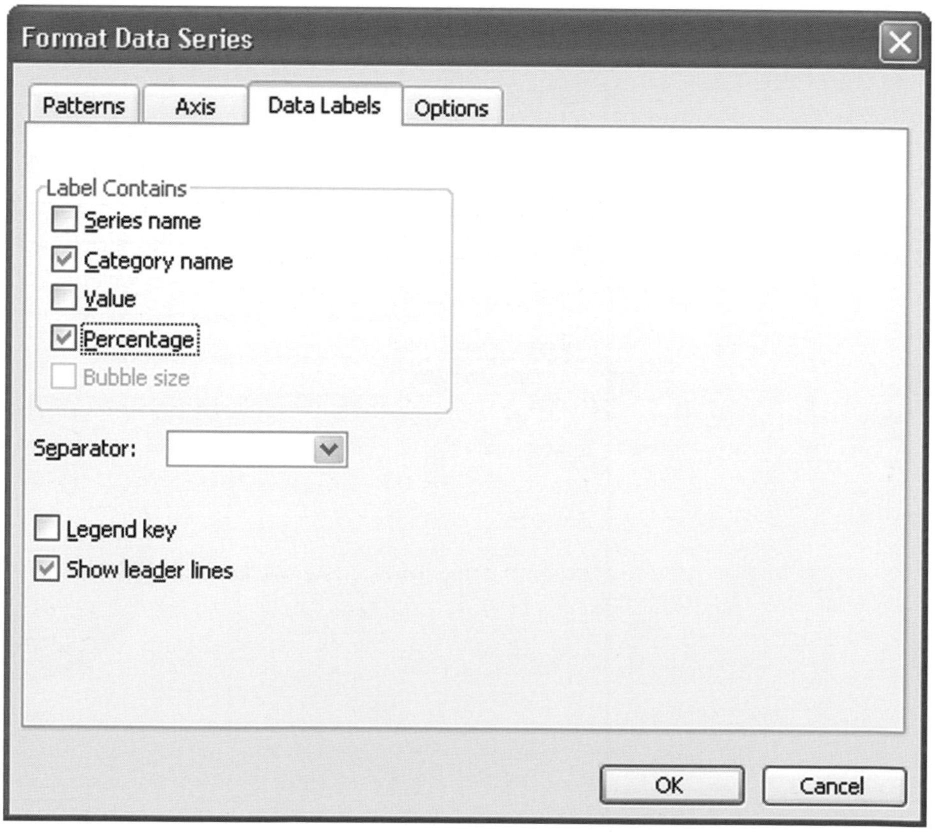

Figure 25   Excel screenshot – Format Data Series screen

This will produce a chart similar to the one shown below.

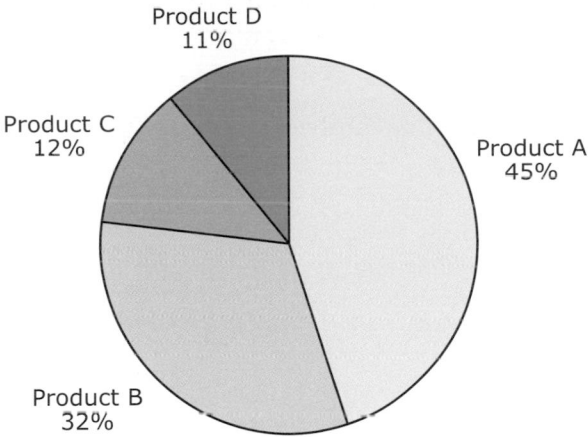

Figure 26 Pie chart produced using an Excel spreadsheet

2.3.2 Producing a bar chart

Step 1 Enter data for the year and total, as you did in Section 2.3.1.

	A	B	C	D	E
1	**Spindle Motors Ltd**				
2	*Sales analysis*				
3		20X1	20X2	20X3	
4		£	£	£	
5	Product A	200,000	210,000	215,000	
6	Product B	140,000	146,000	148,000	
7	Product C	52,000	55,000	57,000	
8	Product D	46,000	47,000	49,000	
9	Total sales	438,000	458,000	469,000	
10					

Highlight the data you wish to appear in the chart. In this case to produce a bar chart showing the 20X1 figures, highlight cells down from A5 to A8 then move the mouse pointer across to highlight cells B5 to B8.

Click on the chart icon on the spreadsheet toolbar, choose the chart type column and choose the appropriate sub-type. The Clustered Column has been chosen as shown in Figure 27.

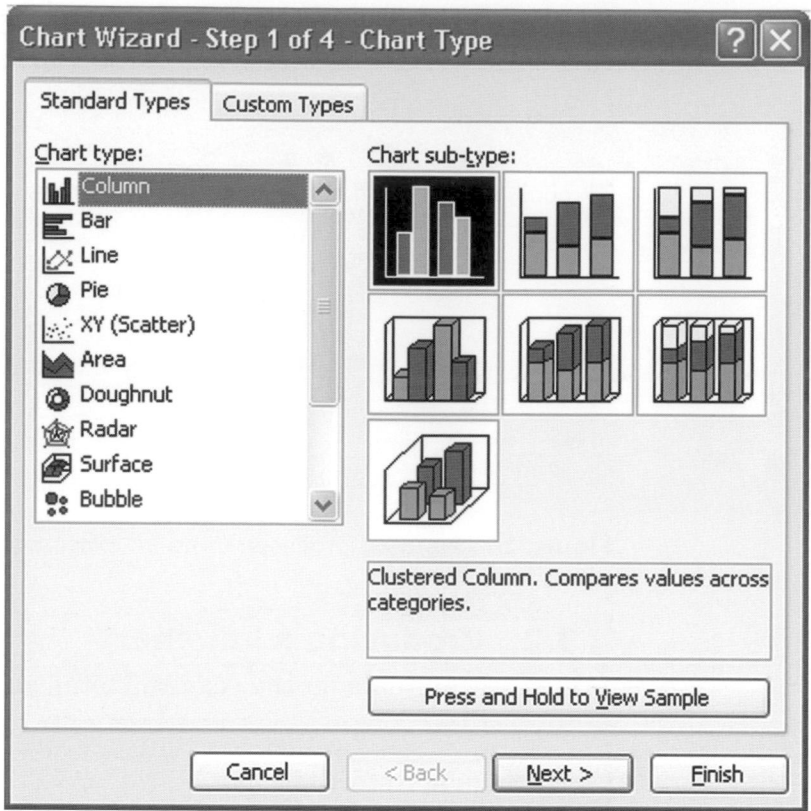

Figure 27   Excel Chart Wizard – Step 1 of 4 – Chart Type

Step 2   Accept the default setting for the Data Range and the Series and click Next.

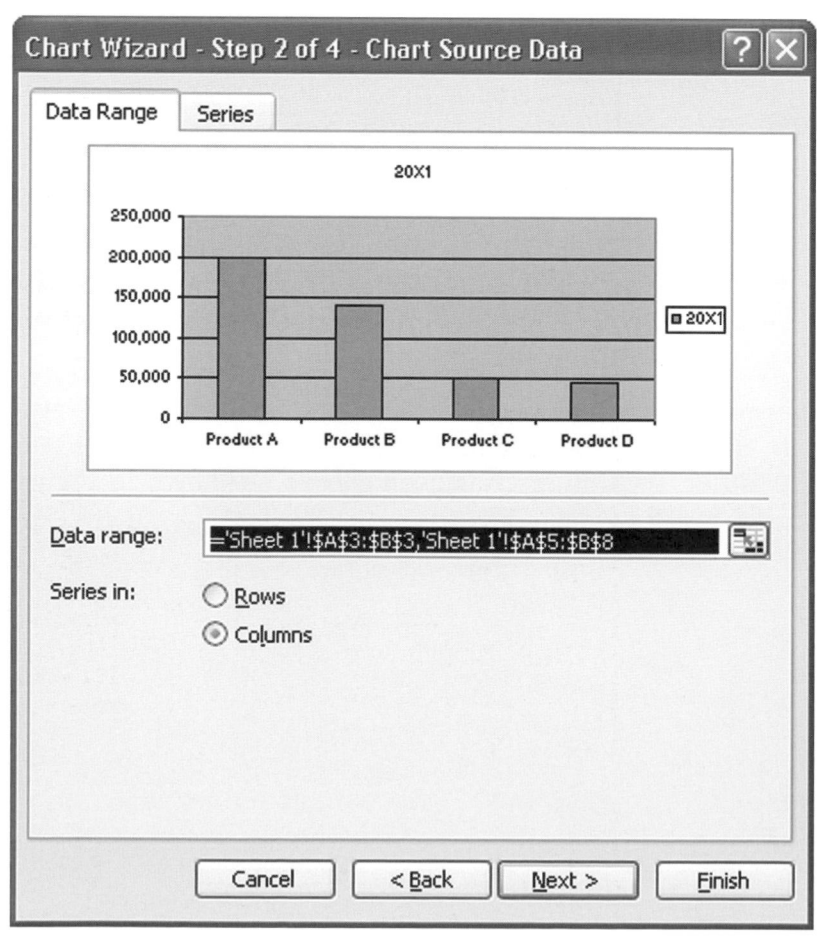

Figure 28   Excel Chart Wizard – Step 2 of 4 – Chart Source Data (Data Range)

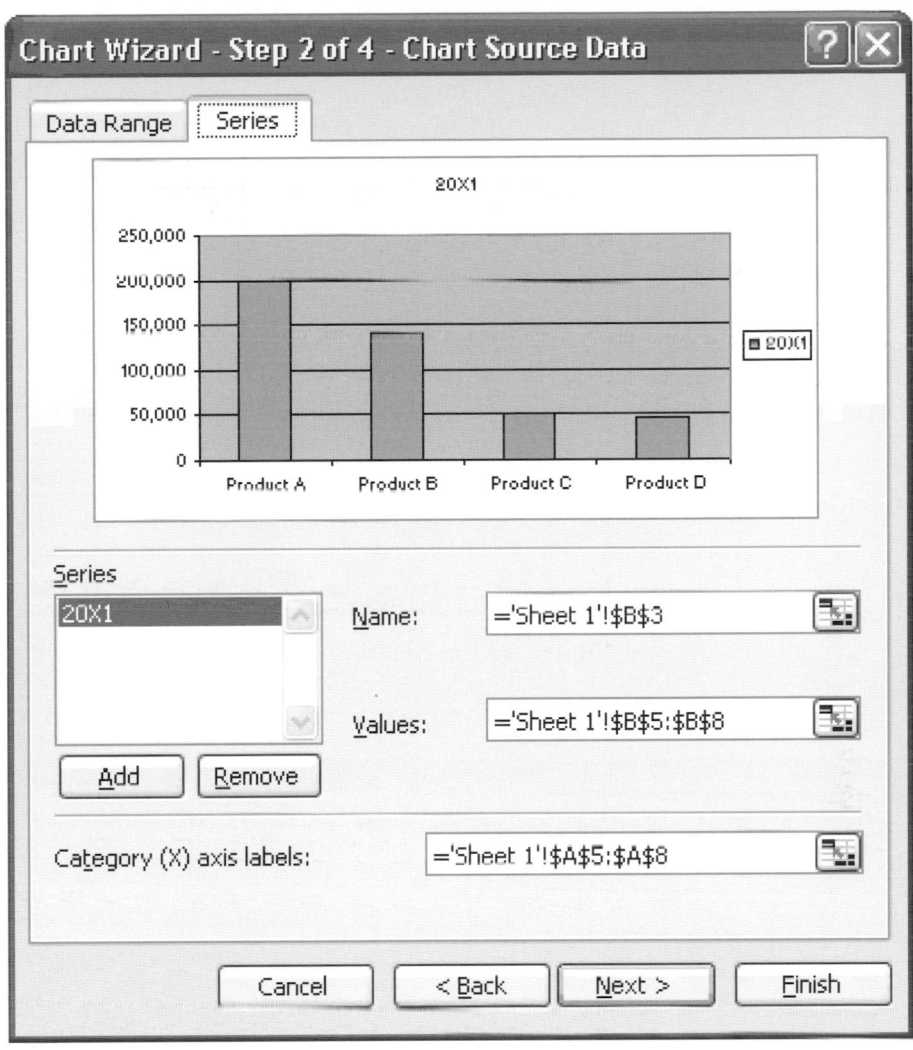

Figure 29   Excel Chart Wizard – Step 2 of 4 – Chart Source Data (Series)

Step 3   Enter in Chart title box 'Sales Analysis'; then enter in Category (X) axis box 'Products'; and then in Value (Y) axis box enter 'Sales'

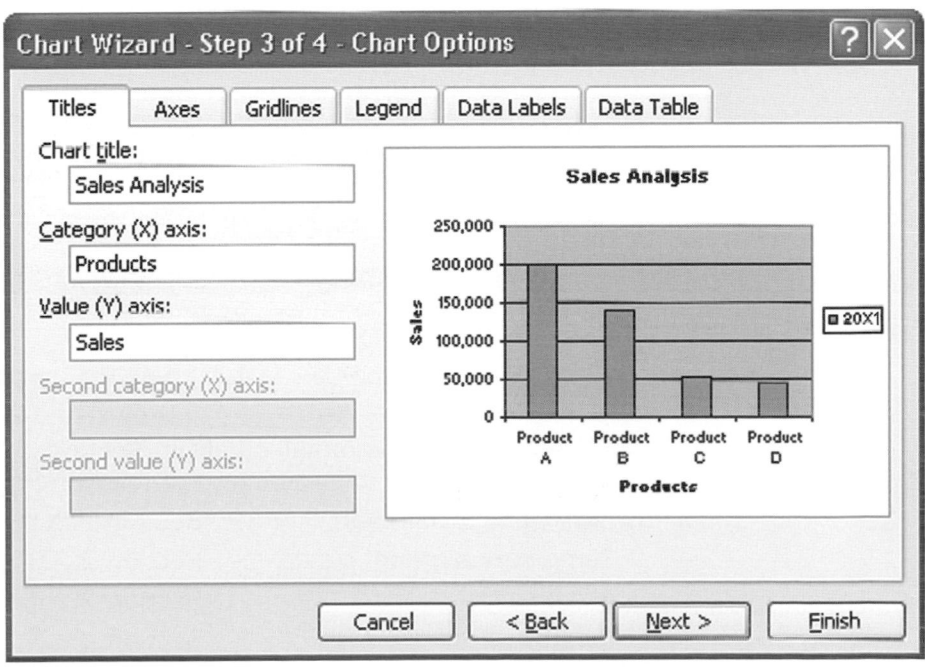

Figure 30   Excel Chart Wizard – Step 3 of 4 – Chart Options (Titles)

Note the other tabs. Experiment with these and then click Next.

Step 4 The next screen (Chart Location) allows you to choose whether you want the chart to appear on the current worksheet along with the data or on a separate sheet. Make your choice and then click Finish.

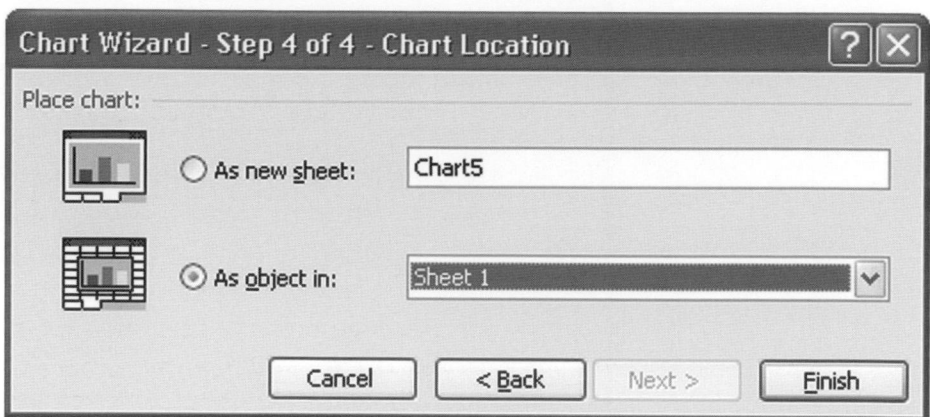

Figure 31 Excel Chart Wizard – Step 4 of 4 – Chart Location

This will produce a chart similar to the one below:

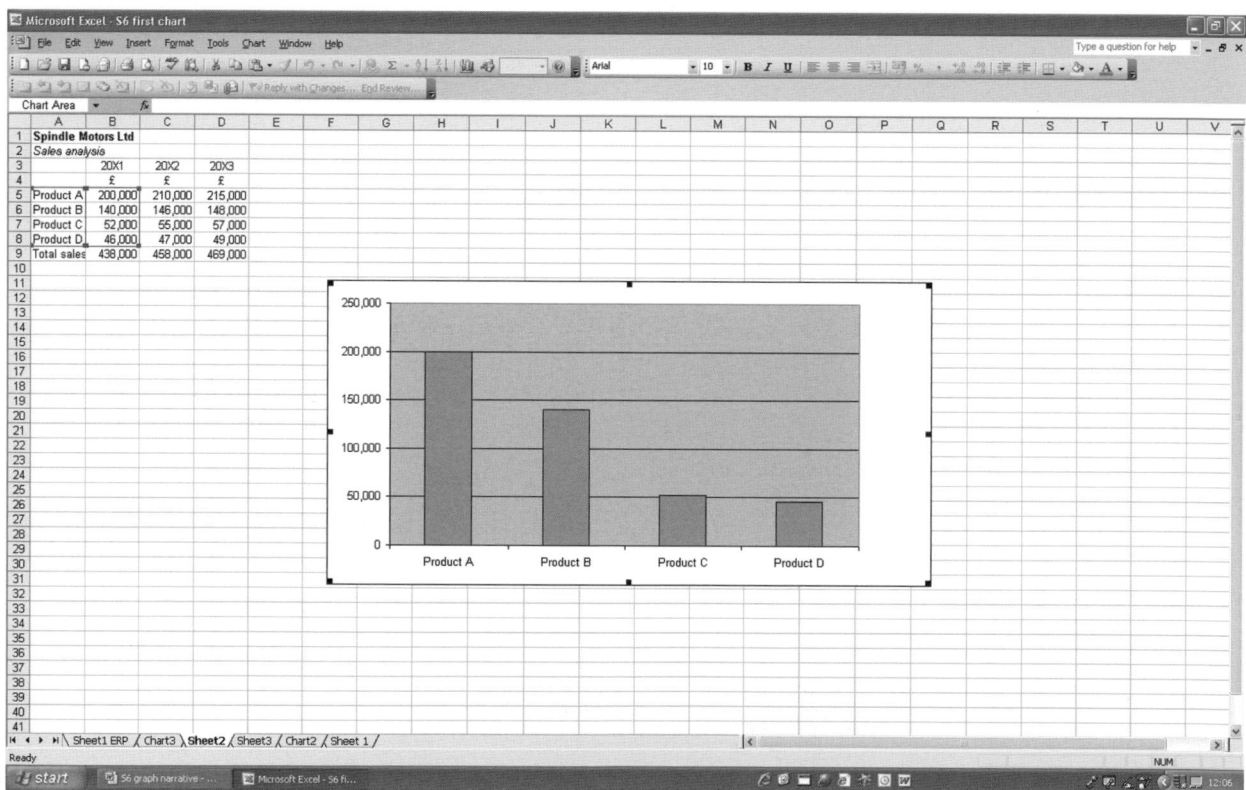

Figure 32 Bar chart produced using an Excel spreadsheet

Activity 2.2

Using the Analysis of sales data in Section 2.1 and the instructions above, see if you can recreate the following graphs and charts:

Component bar chart	Section 2.2.1
Time series graph	Section 2.2.3
Pie chart	Section 2.2.4
Scatter graphs	Section 2.2.5

Spend about 30 minutes doing this.

Feedback ....

All the charts are shown in the text. The following is a reminder of the method to use.

1   Enter the data in the spreadsheet.

	A	B	C
1	Monthly sales		
2			
3	Month	Sales	
4	1	50,000	
5	2	66,000	
6	3	45,000	
7	4	95,000	
8	5	75,000	
9	6	66,000	

2   Click on the Chart Wizard icon on the spreadsheet toolbar.
3   Select chart type.
4   Select the data range and data series.
5   Chart options – choose titles, where the legends are shown and data labels.
6   Choose chart location.

Note that the chart will appear as a bar chart. To remove the spaces between the bars you would do as follows.

(a) Click a single bar on the chart.
(b) The 'Format Data series' screen will appear. Ensure that you are on the 'Options' tab, where you will see two boxes:
   1   Overlap
   2   Gap width.
(c) Enter 0 in the Gap width box.

2.4   Frequency distributions

A **frequency distribution** simply shows how often an event or quantity occurs.

2.4.1   Deriving a frequency distribution

Consider the manager of a furniture manufacturer who is looking at the pattern of deliveries. The following array of raw data (Table 2.1) shows the mileage travelled on consecutive days by a furniture van when making deliveries on the long distance route.

Table 2.1   Array of mileage travelled on consecutive days by a furniture van

521	424	521	411	450	555
400	387	450	348	400	411
488	387	424	387	321	499
321	462	400	501	364	442
364	424	319	356	501	351
587	501	442	365	424	462
501	411	450	543	387	555
399	351	424	336	488	424
424	555	351	356	462	462
442	449	462	400	499	399

However, this table does not help the reader to understand the data. If the data are organised in some way, they can become more meaningful.

Ungrouped frequency distribution

The data can be ordered in terms of size, showing frequency of occurrence.

Table 2.2   Ungrouped frequency distribution

Mileage	Frequency	Mileage	Frequency
319	1	424	7
321	2	442	3
336	1	449	1
348	1	450	3
351	3	462	5
356	2	488	2
364	2	499	2
365	1	501	4
387	4	521	2
399	2	543	1
400	4	555	3
411	3	587	1

This still does not do enough to make the data easy to understand.

Grouped frequency distribution

The data can be simplified further by grouping it into sets of non-overlapping groups.

Table 2.3   Grouped frequency distribution

Mileage	Frequency (*f*)
300 but under 350	5
350 but under 400	14
400 but under 450	18
450 but under 500	12
500 but under 550	7
550 but under 600	4
	60

The differences between the highest and lowest values in each group are known as class intervals. In the grouped frequency distribution above, this is 50 miles. When constructing a frequency table there should be relatively few classes, so that the information contained therein is easy to grasp. However, if there are too few, information will be lost. If possible the width of the class intervals should be equal.

2.5 Histograms

A **histogram** is the graph of a grouped frequency distribution. Frequencies are plotted on the y axis. The other variable (i.e., the one the frequency of occurrence of which is being depicted) is plotted on the x axis.

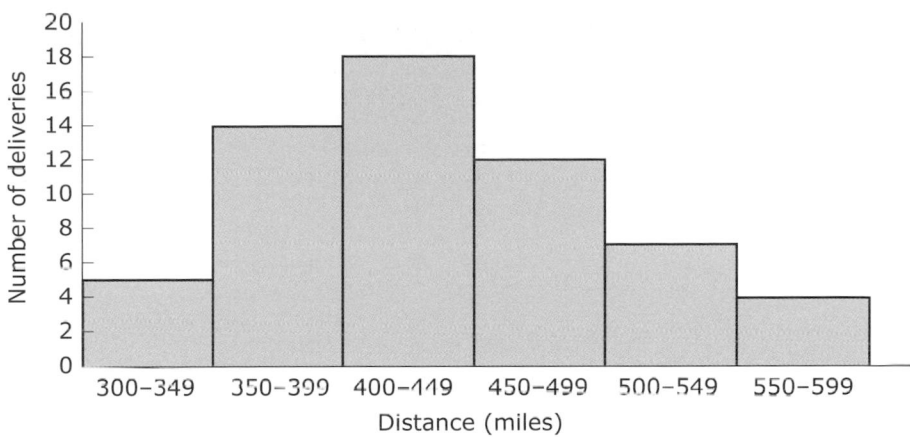

Figure 33 Histogram of furniture deliveries

For histograms, the area under each bar is important, as the frequencies are proportional to area. In Figure 33, the mile intervals are of equal width. This implies that the frequencies are equal to the heights of the vertical column.

2.6 Measures of centrality

This section describes three common measures for determining the location of the central point (centrality) of a distribution: the arithmetic mean, the median and the mode.

2.6.1 Arithmetic mean (known as the mean)

Most people, when asked to calculate an average, would calculate the **arithmetic mean**. They would add up the figures given and divide the total by the number of items. So, if asked to find the average of 60, 30, 20 and 10, the answer given would be (120 ÷ 4) = 30. This is known as the arithmetic mean for a series of numbers.

The arithmetic mean is represented by the symbol $\bar{x}$ (pronounced x bar). It is calculated by adding the values (x) and dividing by the number of values (n)

$$\bar{x} = \frac{\sum x}{n}$$

$\sum$ (Greek capital sigma) is the mathematical symbol meaning 'sum of'.

Looking at a simple example of a sickness reporting system, the mean number of absences during July is calculated by adding up the number of days that each person was absent and then dividing the total by the number of people.

Name	Absences (days)
Mick Brandon	1
Sam Cassimally	0
Sheila Holdsworth	2
Ruby Paparlo	0
Norman Richards	16*
Peter Stevenson	0
May Wong	1

* See 'Weaknesses' at the end of this section.

The total number of days of sickness is therefore:

$$1 + 0 + 2 + 0 + 16 + 0 + 1 = 20 \ (\textstyle\sum x).$$

The number of people (n) is 7, so the mean length of absence in July due to sickness is

$$\bar{x} = \frac{\sum x}{n} = \frac{20}{7} = 2.86 \ \text{days}$$

Weighted average (mean)

Data often need to be weighted by the frequencies of the items before an average can be calculated. Consider a company that sells three products, as follows.

Product	Selling price £
A	10
B	14
C	21

The simple average selling price would be:

$$\frac{10 + 14 + 21}{3} = 15$$

However, this assumes that the company sells all products in equal quantities. This may not be the case. On investigation, you discover that the company sold 100 units of A, 75 units of B and 25 units of C. The **weighted average** selling price needs to reflect these quantities:

$$\text{Weighted average} = \frac{(100 \times 10) + (75 \times 14) + (25 \times 21)}{100 + 75 + 25} = 12.875$$

Alternatively this could be written as:

$$\left(\frac{100}{200} \times 10 \right) + \left(\frac{75}{200} \times 14 \right) + \left(\frac{25}{200} \times 21 \right) = 12.875$$

Arithmetic mean of a grouped frequency distribution

When data are grouped together into classes, detail is lost. In grouped data, the exact values of all items are not known, only the number of values that fit into each class. The method used above to calculate the mean cannot therefore be used when data are grouped together in the form of a frequency distribution.

There are two methods for calculating the mean of a frequency distribution, represented respectively by the following formulae:

$$\bar{x} = \frac{\sum fx}{\sum f} \quad \text{and} \quad \bar{x} = A + \frac{\sum fd}{\sum f}$$

This next example will use the method described below which uses the formula:

$$\bar{x} - A + \frac{\sum fd}{\sum f}$$

where

A is the assumed mean

f represents the frequency, or occurrence, of a particular data item

d is the deviation from the assumed mean

Where figures are large, using an assumed mean ensures that the calculations are less cumbersome than when not using an assumed mean.

Pradeep's furniture shop makes a number of deliveries to customers during a particular period. The deliveries are categorised by the distance from Pradeep's shop, as follows:

Kilometres	Frequency (f)
0–10	20
10–20	45
20–30	85
30–40	50
40–50	15
50–60	5
	220

The assumed mean, A, is 25. This was arrived at by taking the mid-point of the class interval with the highest frequency (20 to 30 kilometres).

Using the formula:

$$\bar{x} = A + \frac{\sum fd}{\sum f}$$

Deliveries		Mid-point		
km	f	x	d	fd
0–10	20	5	–2	–40
10–20	45	15	–1	–45
20–30	85	25	0	0
30–40	50	35	1	50
40–50	15	45	2	30
50–60	5	55	3	15
	$\sum f = 220$			$\sum fd = 10$

x = the mid-point of the deliveries' range, so in the first line the mid-point is 5.

d = the deviation of x from the assumed mean which in this case needs to be divided by the class interval of the deliveries range. The class interval in the deliveries column above is 10 in each case (i.e., 0 to 10, 10 to 20, etc.). In the first line, $x = 5$, so deduct the assumed mean and divide by the class interval of 10, that is, $\dfrac{x-A}{10}$, so $\dfrac{5-25}{10} = -2$.

Provided that the class intervals are the same (in this case 10), d can be divided by the class interval. If they are not the same, this cannot be done.

$$fd = \text{the frequency} \times \text{the deviation}$$

Having completed the table, the mean can be calculated using the formula, remembering to multiply by the class interval (10 in this case):

$$\bar{x} = A + \frac{\sum fd}{\sum f} = 25 + \frac{10}{220} \times 10 = 25.45$$

The arithmetic mean is the most useful form of average. You meet it again later in this session and in Sessions 3 and 4. The arithmetic mean has the following strengths and weaknesses.

Strengths

- It is widely understood.
- It takes into consideration the value of every item in the distribution.
- It can be calculated directly from the raw data (data that have not been organised in some way), unlike the median and the mode.

Weaknesses

- It often gives a value that is not typical of the data from which it was calculated. You may have seen it reported that the average family has 2.2 children but no one can have part of a child.
- It cannot be computed from incomplete data, as the calculation involves adding up all values.
- A potentially misleading value can be obtained if the original data contain extreme values. In the sickness absence example, one person (Norman) has a far higher sickness rate than anyone else. If Norman is not included in the calculation, the mean for the remaining people in the department is 0.67 days: 4 days' absence divided by 6 people. By including the atypical data for Norman, the mean was nearly 3 days of absence per person (20 ÷ 7 = 2.86 days), as opposed to about two thirds of a day when he was not included. An atypical data item can make quite a difference.

2.6.2   Median

The **median** is the middle value once all the values are arranged in ascending order.

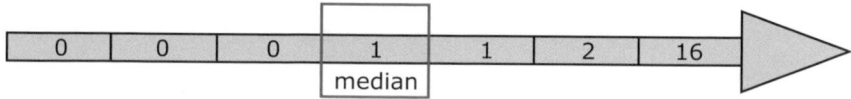

Figure 34   The median

The absence figures from Section 2.6.1 can be rearranged in order of size to give the median range in Figure 34.

There are seven figures, so the middle one is the fourth value which is 1. So, using the median, you could say that the average number of days of sickness in the department is 1. Again, this seems a reasonable figure since a couple of people did have one day's sickness and most of the others had either none or two.

Here is another example. The median of 26, 48, 72, 87 and 96 is 72.

The rule is that the median is the $\frac{n+1}{2}$ th item so, if there are 153 items, the median is the 77th item.

If the number of items is even, then the rule is to take the arithmetic mean of the two middle numbers (i.e., divide the sum of the two middle numbers by 2). The median of 34, 47, 56, 63, 84 and 92 is 59.5, that is, the mean of 56 and 63.

The median has the following strengths and weaknesses.

Strengths

- It is easily understood by people who have no mathematical background.

- It gives a typical value (usually but not always, as shown above), since you are picking one of the actual data items to use as a representative.

- It is not affected by extreme values: you can always find the middle number.

- It can be applied when numerical values are difficult to obtain, as long as the items can be put in order. For example, you may wish to find out the average salary of managers in your company. You may not be able to find out the salary of the highest paid managers; however, you may be able to find out the salaries of the others.

Weaknesses

- The median cannot be used in further arithmetical calculations (statistical analysis) and is therefore of limited practical use. You will not meet it again in this unit other than in Activity 2.3 and in Session 4 when looking at the **normal distribution curve**.

- Arranging the data into ascending order manually may be tedious.

- If there are only data available for a few items, the calculated median is unlikely to be representative.

2.6.3 Mode

The **mode** is the data item that occurs most frequently.

In the sickness absences example, the mean is 2.86 days (20 ÷ 7). In contrast, the most common number of days absence is 0 and so the mode is 0. This is, arguably, a fairer indication than the mean of the true pattern of attendance by the seven people in the department over the period observed. Most of them have had very little absence or no absence from work through sickness. Using the mode rather than the mean results in the average (as given by the mode) being unaffected by Norman's prolonged absence.

In another example, the sales of ladies' jackets, it can be seen that the mode is size 14.

Number of purchases	Size	
400	10	
550	12	
600	**14**	◄— **Mode**
450	16	
300	18	
200	20	

In this example, knowing the mode will help the shop owner in his/her inventory management in deciding which inventory item to purchase in greater quantity.

The mode has the following strengths and weaknesses.

Strengths

- The mode, like the median, gives a typical value (unlike the mean, which can give an impossible value – a fractional number of days in the sickness example).

- It can be used to give the average of **category variables**. Category variables are variables that are not numbers but descriptions, such as 'married', 'divorced', 'widowed', etc. Since the variables are not numbers, it would be meaningless to calculate a 'mean' but it is possible to give the most frequently occurring category.

- It is easily understood.

- It is unaffected by extreme values.

Weaknesses

- There can be more than one mode within a set of data.

- It records only the most frequently recurring item(s). No other values are taken into account in its derivation, unlike the mean, which includes all the data in its calculation.

- It has fewer applications, as it is only meaningful when there is a cluster of values around a single point.

Now check your ability to calculate the various types of averages by completing the following activity. Once you have completed it, check that you understand the methods before moving on to Section 2.7 'Measures of dispersion'.

Activity 2.3 ··

A chain of shoe shops is trying to decide which shoe sizes to order to ensure that it stocks the most popular sizes. It has monitored shoe sales for a week in one of its branches and produced the following data.

Shoe size	Number of pairs sold
3	10
4	21
5	36
6	27
7	12
8	18
9	25
10	15
11	3
12	1
13	0
	168

The shop wants to determine the average size of shoe sold.

From the frequency distribution determine the following:

(a) weighted average mean

(b) median

(c) mode.

Comment on the usefulness of each of these results to the shoe shop chain.

Spend about 20 minutes on this activity.

Feedback ....

(a) Weighted average mean = 6.57 (to two decimal places)

$$(3 \times 10) + (4 \times 21) + (5 \times 36) + (6 \times 27) + (7 \times 12) + (8 \times 18) + (9 \times 25) + (10 \times 15) + (11 \times 3) + (12 \times 1) = 1,104$$

So the weighted average mean is $\dfrac{1,104}{168} = 6.5714285$.

(b) Median = 6. The shoes sizes are already arranged in order of magnitude. Half the frequency is $\dfrac{84 + 85}{2} = 84.5$. (As the number of items is even, divide the sum of the two middle numbers, 84 and 85, by two.) The 84.5^{th} item is a size 6 shoe.

Shoe size	Number of pairs sold	Cumulative frequency
3	10	10
4	21	31
5	36	67
6	27	94
7	12	
8	18	
9	25	
10	15	
11	3	
12	1	
13	0	
	168	

The mean of the two middle numbers

$$= \frac{84 + 85}{2} = 84.5$$

(c) Mode = 5. More size 5 shoes are sold than any other, that is, 36 pairs.

The mode is probably the most useful so that the shop staff know what to stock in great quantity. In this case it is clear that measures of central location alone would not be sufficient in planning inventory holdings.

2.7 Measures of dispersion

In Section 2.6 the underlying averages (mean, median and mode), which give an indication of where data is clustered, were considered, but clustering is not enough to give a clear understanding of the data. It is important to know about the spread (or dispersion) of the data items around the averages. Are the items in the distribution concentrated closely together or are they widely spread out around the average? This section looks at some widely used measures of spread or dispersion: the range, the standard deviation, variance and coefficient of variation.

2.7.1   Range

The **range** is simply the difference between the highest and lowest items in the population:

$$\text{range} = x_{\max} - x_{\min}$$

If there were a distribution where the highest reading was 16 and the lowest 2, a manager might say the range was '2 to 16' (a statistician, however, would say the range was '14' (i.e., $16 - 2$).

The range is therefore a very crude measure of dispersion, as it does not take account of all the data but only looks at the highest and lowest items. Between the two extremes, these data could be widely spread out, clustered at one end or in the middle. This measure is therefore not suitable for further statistical analysis.

2.7.2   Standard deviation (σ, pronounced sigma)

Two sets of data may have the same mean but may have a widely differing dispersion. For example, the data sets 50, 60 and 70 and 3, 60 and 117 both have a mean of 60 but the second set has a much greater spread. The standard deviation allows this to be measured.

The **standard deviation** is the most important measure of dispersion, as it measures average dispersion of data from the mean of the same data. It is calculated from the deviations, or distances, of each item from the arithmetic mean. The more the individual values differ from the mean, the greater the standard deviation will be. Here are two examples.

1   A share price with a high standard deviation varies more than a share price with a low standard deviation.

2   If the output from two machines has different standard deviations, the machine the output of which has the lower standard deviation is the more precise.

The standard deviation of ungrouped data

The formula for the standard deviation of ungrouped data is:

$$\sigma = \sqrt{\frac{\sum (x - \bar{x})^2}{n}}$$

where $(x - \bar{x})$ is the distance of each value from the mean and n is the number of values.

Here is how to calculate the standard deviation σ, using the numbers 2, 3, 5 and 6 as an example.

The mean ($\bar{x}$) is $\dfrac{16}{4} = 4$.

Data value	x	2	3	5	6	
Deviation	$(x - \bar{x})$	-2	-1	1	2	
Deviation squared	$(x - \bar{x})^2$	4	1	1	4	$\Sigma(x - \bar{x})^2 = 10$

▲ Sum of deviations squared

$$\sigma = \sqrt{\frac{\sum (x - \bar{x})^2}{n}} = \sqrt{\frac{10}{4}} = 1.58 \ \text{(to two decimal places)}$$

You might like to check this calculation with your scientific calculator.

It is more usual to set the information out in a vertical format as demonstrated in the next example.

	x	$(x - \bar{x})$	$(x - \bar{x})^2$
	3	-5	25
	9	1	1
	12	4	16
Σ	24	Σ	42

Mean = 24/3 = 8.

$$\sigma = \sqrt{\frac{\sum (x - \bar{x})^2}{n}} = \sqrt{\frac{42}{3}} = \sqrt{14} = 3.74$$

If you look at the equation, you will see that the square of the difference between a particular reading and the mean is used. (Squaring is a typical mathematical way of getting rid of minuses, which is useful when only a measure of difference itself is needed.) All the squared differences are added and the sum divided by the number of readings. So the mean of the data is first calculated, then an 'average squared difference' of a reading from the mean is worked out to give an idea of how spread out the readings are around the mean (before calculating the standard deviation).

The standard deviation of a frequency distribution

Here the above formula is simply modified to give:

$$\sigma = \sqrt{\frac{\sum f(x - \bar{x})^2}{n}}$$

The mileage travelled in week 32 by a company's salesmen is shown below:

Table 2.4 Miles travelled by salesmen over a seven day period

Mileage	Frequency of trips
20	2
24	4
32	3
43	8
51	1
60	5
64	2
	25

Calculate the standard deviation per trip for the week and compare it with the previous week's standard deviation per trip of 5.7.

x	f	fx	$(x - \bar{x})$	$(x - \bar{x})^2$	$f(x - \bar{x})^2$
20	2	40	−22.2	492.84	985.68
24	4	96	−18.2	331.24	1,324.96
32	3	96	−10.2	104.04	312.12
43	8	344	0.8	0.64	5.12
51	1	51	8.8	77.44	77.44
60	5	300	17.8	316.84	1,584.20
64	2	128	21.8	475.24	950.48
294	25	1,055			5,240

Mean $\bar{x} = \sum \dfrac{fx}{f} = \dfrac{1,055}{25} = 42.2$

$$\sigma = \sqrt{\dfrac{\sum f(x - \bar{x})^2}{\sum f}} = \sqrt{\dfrac{5,240}{25}} = \sqrt{209.6} = 14.48 \text{ (to 4 significant figures)}$$

Comparing this with the previous week's standard deviation, you can see that there is a wider spread of mileage per trip travelled by salesmen in week 32 compared with week 31.

The standard deviation of a grouped frequency distribution

The arithmetic mean of a grouped frequency distribution could be calculated using the formula above but taking the mid-point of the class to represent that class. There is, however, an easier formula for the mean, which involves taking an assumed mean and calculating the deviations from that mean.

Here is the data on the furniture shop deliveries in Section 2.6.1:

A grouped frequency covers a range of values, for example, 0 to under 10, 10 to under 20, etc.

Kilometres	Frequency (f)
0 to under 10	20
10 to under 20	45
20 to under 30	85
30 to under 40	50
40 to under 50	15
50 to under 60	5
	220

First, calculate the mean. This was calculated in Section 2.6.1 as 25.45.

$$\bar{x} = A + \dfrac{\sum fd}{\sum f} = 25 + \dfrac{10}{220} \times 10 = 25.45$$

Then deduct the mean from x (see column 4 in the next table), square the deviations (column 5), then multiply by the frequency (column 3) and add up (columns 3 and 6).

(1)	(2)	(3)	(4)	(5)	(6)
Deliveries (km)	Mid-point x	f	$(x - \bar{x})$	$(x - \bar{x})^2$	$f(x - \bar{x})^2$
0–10	5	20	−20.45	418.20	8,364
10–20	15	45	−10.45	109.20	4,914
20–30	25	85	−0.45	0.20	17
30–40	35	50	9.55	91.20	4,560
40–50	45	15	19.55	382.20	5,733
50–60	55	5	29.55	873.20	4,366
		220			27,954

Now apply the standard deviation equation, $\sigma = \sqrt{\dfrac{\sum f(x - \bar{x})^2}{\sum f}}$:

$$\sigma = \sqrt{\frac{\sum f(x - \bar{x})^2}{\sum f}} = \sqrt{\frac{27,954}{220}} = \sqrt{127.0636364} = 11.272$$

The standard deviation measures how far each piece of data is from the mean and calculates an average deviation from that. The larger the standard deviation, the greater the dispersion of values will be from the mean. The standard deviation allows comparison between sets of data, as you will see in the self-assessed question on this topic at the end of the unit.

Standard deviation of a sample (s)

Everything above is based on the whole population of data. In circumstances where the whole population is not known and a sample is taken to estimate characteristics of the population, the formula for the standard deviation becomes:

This can also be written as

$$s = \sqrt{\frac{\sum (x - \bar{x})^2}{n - 1}}$$

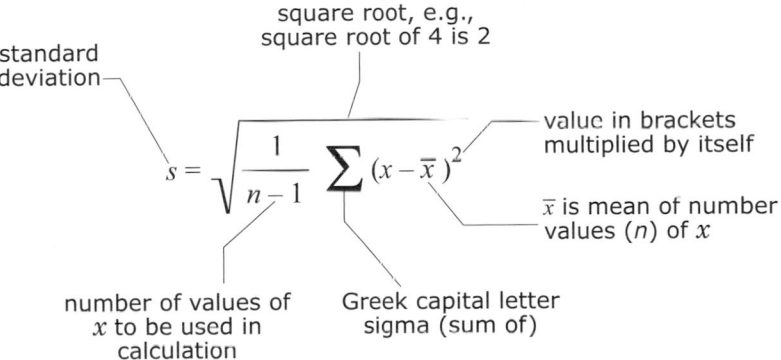

Figure 35   Standard deviation of a sample

The standard deviation has the following strengths and weaknesses.

Strengths

- The standard deviation uses every value in the distribution.
- It is a very useful and important measure, as it can be used for further statistical analysis. (You will meet this again in Section 4.3 when the normal distribution curve is discussed.)

Weaknesses

- It is more difficult to understand/comprehend than other measures of dispersion, such as the range.
- It gives more than proportional weight to extreme values as it squares the deviations.

Now try the following activity.

Activity 2.4 ··

Look at the figures for waiting times to see an adviser in two building societies, A and B.

Table 2.5   Waiting times

Society A waiting time (minutes)	Society B waiting time (minutes)
10	9
9.5	9
26	10
8	11
12.5	9.5
11	9
9	8
2	10
21	13
16	12
6	7
3	10
15	9
4.5	8.5
8	9.5
10	9.5
10.5	8
12	9
8.5	10
7.5	12
12	11
6	8.5
3	10
14	8
11	7.5
2	9.5
1.5	10
8.5	8.5
8	10
9	9

(a) What is the mean waiting time at each society?

(b) What is the mode at each society?

(c) What is the median at each society?

(d) What is the range of waiting times at each society?

(e) What is the standard deviation in waiting times at each society?

(f) Using the results of your calculations in parts (a) to (e), if the only difference between the two building societies was the waiting times, which society would you prefer to use? Explain why.

Spend about 30 minutes on this activity.

Feedback

(a) The mean = $\frac{\Sigma x}{n}$. The Σx is 285 in both cases and n is 30 in both cases. The mean for Society A is 9.5 minutes and for Society B it is also 9.5 minutes.

(b) The mode is the number that occurs most. The mode for Society A is 8 minutes and for Society B it is 10 minutes.

(c) The median is the $\frac{n+1}{2}$ item. The median for Society A is 9 minutes and for Society B it is 9.5 minutes.

(d) The range for Society A is 24.5 (i.e., 26 – 1.5) minutes and for Society B it is 6 (i.e., 13 – 7) minutes.

(e) The standard deviation = $\sqrt{\frac{\Sigma(x - \bar{x})^2}{n}}$. The standard deviation for Society A is $\sqrt{\frac{848.5}{30}} = 5.3$ and for Society B it is $\sqrt{\frac{52.2}{30}} = 1.3$.

(f) The measures of central location (mean, mode and median) in this case indicate very little difference between the two building societies. However, the measures of spread (dispersion), such as the standard deviation, indicate that there is a much greater variability for Society A than Society B. This may indicate that there is a chance that the waiting time is very low for Society A. However, it could also be high. In the case of Society B, you can be reasonably confident about how long you will have to wait. The choice as to which you would choose, however, is a matter of personal preference. Would you take the chance of a long wait in the hope that you might be seen quickly (Society A), or would you prefer the waiting time to be more predictable (Society B)? A lower standard deviation is better for planning purposes.

2.7.3   Variance (σ^2)

The **variance** is an important part of many statistical applications and analyses. It measures the variability (volatility) from an average, and is often used in assessment of risk (such as that associated with purchasing investments). The variance is the square of the standard deviation. For example, a standard deviation of 4.25 gives a variance of 18 (to the nearest whole number).

The important feature of variances is that they can be added (provided that the data come from the same population), while standard deviations cannot. Therefore, to find the overall standard deviation of two data sets expressed in the same unit (e.g., kilos), the variance of each set can be found, the two variances added together and the square root of the result taken. For example:

Distribution	Variance	Standard deviation
x	18	4.25
y	13	3.61
$x + y$	31	$\sqrt{31} = 5.57$

If you had added the two standard deviations of 4.25 and 3.61 together, you would get an incorrect answer of 7.86.

2.7.4   Coefficient of variation

There are occasions when the degree of variation between two or more sets of figures expressed in differing units (years, kilos, miles, metres, etc.) needs to be compared. The **coefficient of variation** (also known as the coefficient of dispersion) allows the degree of variation between different distributions to be compared, as it indicates the amount of variability present in the data. For example, it can be used to find out whether the weight of a group of people varies more or less than their heights; or whether the average bonuses of UK bankers (expressed in £) varies more or less than the average bonuses of USA bankers (expressed in $).

The coefficient of variation is the ratio of the standard deviation (σ) of a distribution to the mean ($\bar{x}$) of the distribution, expressed as a percentage.

$$\text{Coefficient of variation} = \frac{\sigma}{\bar{x}} \times 100$$

The larger the coefficient of variation, the wider the spread of the data.

Two distributions display the following characteristics:

Distribution 1 $\sigma = 10.8$ $\bar{x} = 70.5$ lbs

Distribution 2 $\sigma = 3.4$ $\bar{x} = 29.6$ litres

As the figures are expressed in different units (i.e., one in weight and the other in volume), the variance cannot be used to compare them, although they can be compared using the coefficient of variation.

Coefficient of variation for distribution 1 is $\dfrac{10.8}{70.5} \times 100 = 15.3\%$

Coefficient of variation for distribution 2 is $\dfrac{3.4}{29.6} \times 100 = 11.5\%$

Distribution 1 has the larger coefficient of variation, which shows that the data are more widely spread than in distribution 2, that is, there is more relative variability in the data in distribution 1 compared with distribution 2.

Spreadsheet: averages and measures of dispersion

Measures of centrality and measures of dispersion can be calculated using a spreadsheet (although in the examination you will need to be able to calculate them manually).

For example, a company's share has been quoted on the London Stock Exchange at the following prices (in pence):

136	130	133	115	139	129	141	148
138	136	127	124	130	133	137	150
137	132	116	131	126	145	152	140
135	134	123	122	140	132	144	146
134	137	124	121	126	141	138	147

To calculate the various measures of centrality and dispersion we:
- first, enter the data on a spreadsheet (see the following example)
- then enter the word Mean in cell A9, Mode in cell A10, Median in cell A11, Minimum in cell A12, Maximum in cell A13, Range in cell A14, Standard deviation in cell A15, Variance in cell A16
- then enter the various functions in the cell next to each word.

	A	B	C	D	E	F	G	H
1	Share prices							
2	136	130	133	115	139	129	141	148
3	138	136	127	124	130	133	137	150
4	137	132	116	131	126	145	152	140
5	135	134	123	122	140	132	144	146
6	134	137	124	121	126	141	138	147
7								
8								
9	Mean	134.225						
10	Mode	137						
11	Median	134.5						
12	Minimum	115						
13	Maximum	152						
14	Range	37						
15	Standard deviation	8.977143						
16	Variance	80.5891						

Then enter

- In cell B9 enter the average function: = AVERAGE(A2:H6)
- In cell B10 enter the mode function: = MODE(A2:H6)
- In cell B11 enter the median function: = MEDIAN(A2:H6)
- In cell B12 enter the Min function: = MIN(A2:H6)
- In cell B13 enter the Max function: = MAX(A2:H6)
- In cell B14 enter the maximum less the minimum so: = B13-B12
- In cell B15 enter the STDEV function: = STDEV(A2:H6)
- In cell B16 enter the VAR function: = VAR(A2:H6)

Note that the cell references in the brackets above can be obtained by highlighting all the cells with data in. So type the bracket, highlight the cells and then add a closing bracket.

Activity 2.5

Sally is holding a party and has been checking the prices of fruit for a fruit salad. She has looked in 10 shops in the area and the prices are listed below:

Fruit prices in 10 shops

Shop	A	B	C	D	E	F	G	H	I	J
Fruit	£	£	£	£	£	£	£	£	£	£
Bananas (per kg)	0.49	0.49	0.69	0.74	0.84	0.89	0.94	0.99	1.19	1.29
Grapes (per kg)	3.99	1.99	2.49	2.49	2.99	2.99	2.99	3.49	3.99	2.99
Pineapples (each)	2.29	1.99	1.99	1.49	1.79	1.84	1.99	1.99	2.29	1.99
Apples (per kg)	1.24	1.19	1.24	1.29	1.34	1.39	1.44	1.45	1.49	1.59
Strawberries (per 400g)	1.24	1.39	1.49	1.64	1.24	1.69	1.69	1.74	1.74	1.99

(a) Calculate the mean, standard deviation and coefficient of variation for bananas manually.

(b) For every other item of fruit, calculate, either manually or using your computer spreadsheet, the mean, standard deviation and coefficient of variance. The Excel function for calculating the standard deviation is =STDEV, and for calculating the coefficient of variation is the standard deviation divided by the average (=B9/B15×100).

Spend about 35 minutes on this activity.

Feedback

(a) Using the standard deviation of a sample formula, the detailed workings for bananas are:

x	$x - \bar{x}$	$(x - \bar{x})^2$
0.49	(0.365)	0.133225
0.49	(0.365)	0.133225
0.69	(0.165)	0.027225
0.74	(0.115)	0.013225
0.84	(0.015)	0.000225
0.89	0.0350	0.001225
0.94	0.0850	0.007225
0.99	0.1350	0.018225
1.19	0.3350	0.112225
1.29	0.4350	0.189225
Σ 8.55		0.635250

Mean: $\bar{x} = 0.855$

Standard deviation: $s = \sqrt{\dfrac{\sum (x - \bar{x})^2}{n - 1}} = \sqrt{\dfrac{0.635250}{9}} = 0.265675$

Note that this is a sample (see also list of formulae).

Coefficient of variation is $\dfrac{s}{\bar{x}} \times 100 = \dfrac{0.265675}{0.855} \times 100 = 31.0731$

(b) The results for the bananas and all other items are shown below, to two decimal places:

	Mean	SD	CV
Bananas (per kg)	0.86	0.27	31.07
Grapes (per kg)	3.04	0.64	21.16
Pineapples (each)	1.97	0.23	11.83
Apples (per kg)	1.37	0.13	9.38
Strawberries (per 400g)	1.59	0.24	15.20

The figures opposite were calculated using a spreadsheet. Note that if you do this using a calculator, you might get slightly different figures because of roundings.

It is apparent from the results above that there is more variability in the price of bananas and grapes than other fruit, while apples have the least variability in price.

The main strength of the coefficient of variation is that it allows two distributions measured in different units, for example, in profit and units of output, to be compared. This is its key advantage.

Summary

In this session you saw how data can be summarised in tables and presented by using charts in the form of simple bar charts, pie charts, histograms and line graphs, time series graphs and scatter graphs to present the tabulated data. You then looked at how measures of centrality in the form of the mean, mode and median, and measures of dispersion, namely, range, standard deviation, variance and coefficient of variation can be used to represent data. In Session 3 some of the learning from this session will be built on by looking at correlation analysis, regression analysis and forecasting.

SESSION **3 Correlation, regression and forecasting**

Introduction

Upon completion of Session 3, you are expected to be able to:

- understand the nature of dependent and independent variables
- understand the nature and limitations of measures of correlation
- calculate and interpret the correlation coefficient and the coefficient of determination between two variables
- use the scatter graph method to work out the line of best fit in a linear relationship between two variables
- calculate the equation of a straight line from a line of best fit
- use the least squares method in linear regression analysis to forecast the value of the dependent variable
- understand the limitations of linear analysis for forecasting
- adjust time series data for any seasonal variations and extrapolate the trend.

This session looks at correlation and linear regression to help to understand the relationship between two variables and how that information can be used in forecasting. It builds on the knowledge of scatter graphs gained in Section 2.2.5.

3.1 Dependent and independent variables

In business, understanding how one variable influences another is an important part of planning. That there is a relationship between some variables, such as miles driven by a lorry and diesel fuel used, is obvious. Also, managers have found that there is a relationship between the amount spent on advertising and sales volume. There is also likely to be a close relationship between the number of house building plans passed by a local authority and the number of kitchen sinks purchased in the following year.

When looking at the relationship between two variables, it is important to know which is the dependent and which the independent variable, that is, which variable changes in response to changes in the other variable.

Changes in the independent variable cause changes in the dependent variable. If you have a clear idea that the dependency is a particular way round, then it is usual to plot the dependent variable – for example, sales levels – on the (vertical) y axis on a graph, while the independent variable – for example, advertising spend – is plotted on the (horizontal) x axis of a graph. Likewise with the two variables, output and electricity cost, output will be the independent variable (x axis) and electricity cost the dependent variable (y axis), as electricity costs are incurred by producing output.

Often it is not easy or possible to make any assumption about which variable depends on which. Consider advertising: does an increase in advertising costs cause a particular increase in the volume of sales? Does a particular sales level encourage an increase in advertising? It is usual that advertising increases the level of sales, although increased sales can indirectly affect the level of advertising.

3.2 Correlation coefficient (*r*)

There are several different correlation coefficients, often named after people who were instrumental in their development. Karl Pearson developed what became known as Pearson's correlation coefficient in the 1880s.

Pearson's **correlation coefficient** (also known as product moment correlation) describes how two variables move together. Before calculating the correlation coefficient, it is useful to try to form an opinion as to whether it is likely that the two variables are correlated. By plotting the points on a scatter graph, any pattern that indicates a correlation can often be seen quite easily.

The data below show the heights and ages of a group of children.

Heights and ages of children

Age (years)	Height (cm)
2	75
3	81
4	96
4	102
5	90
5	120
6	106
6	122

When this is plotted on a scatter graph, it can be seen that there seems to be some sort of close relationship between age and height, as the points are more or less in a straight line as opposed to being scattered widely in a kind of cloud.

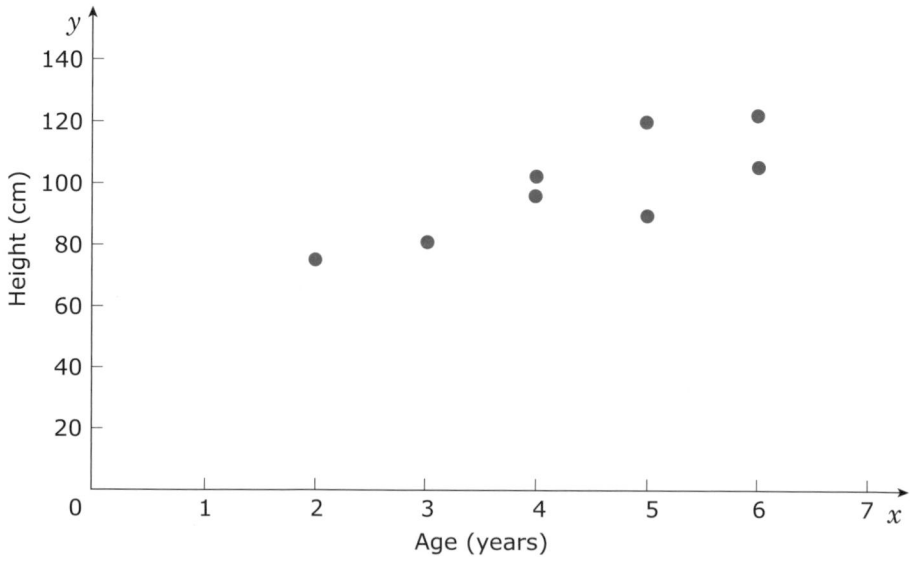

Age was plotted on the x-axis because height depends (partly) on a child's age.

Figure 36   Scatter graph for height and ages of a group of children

The correlation coefficient (r) is always a number from –1 to +1. If it is 0, there is no correlation between the variables, that is, there is no association whatsoever between them. The closer to 0, the less close the relationship.

- **Positive correlation** exists when an increase in one variable is associated to a greater or lesser extent with an increase in the other variable. For example, an increase in advertising could be associated with an increase in sales, and an increase in umbrella sales could be associated with an increase in rain.

- **Negative correlation** exists when an increase in one variable is associated to a greater or lesser extent with a decrease in the other variable. For example, as a student's study time on B292 increases, the number of errors made by the student in the B292 examination is likely to decrease. As the weight of a car increases, the fuel economy decreases.

- **Perfect correlation** (+1 and –1) exists when there is an exact linear relationship between the two variables, that is, all the points lie on a straight line. With perfect correlation, if the quantity of one variable is known, the value of the other variable can be calculated with certainty.

The following scatter graphs illustrate the different types of correlation.

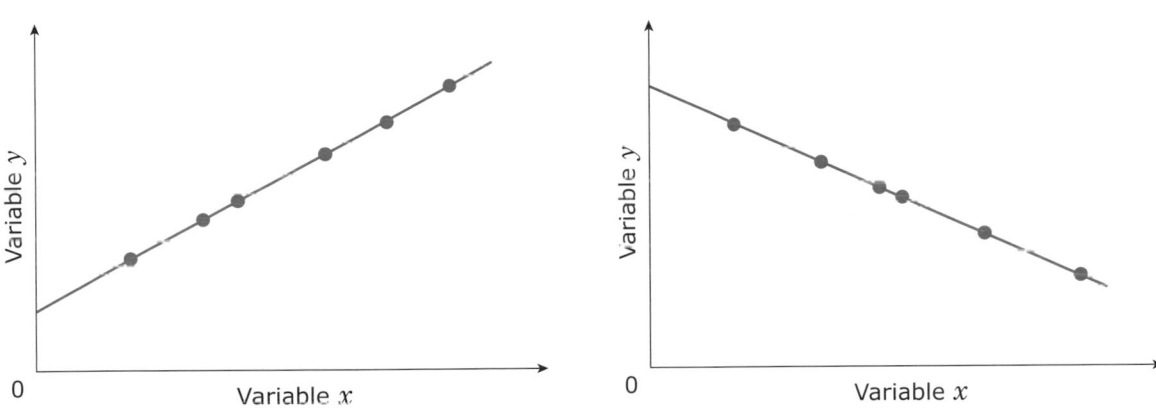

Figure 37   (a) Perfect positive correlation ($r = 1$)   (b) Perfect negative correlation ($r = -1$)

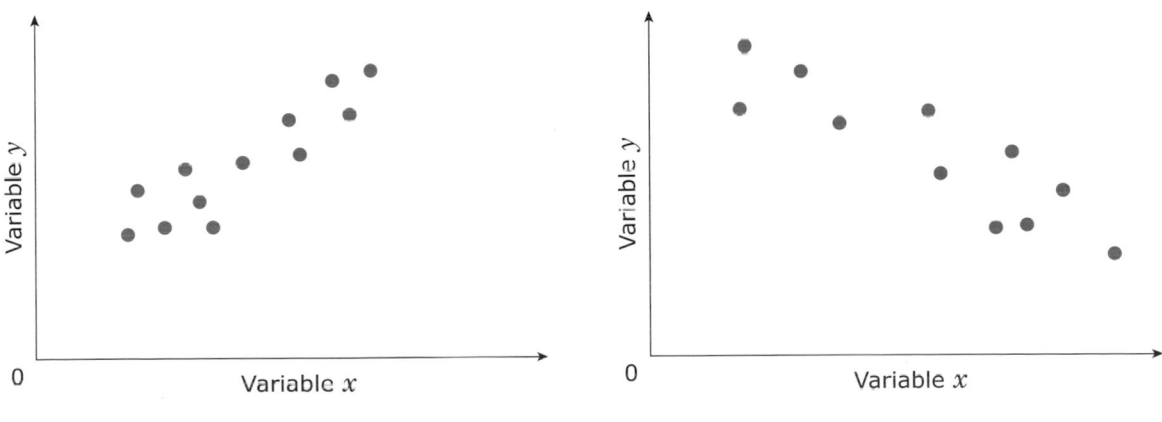

Figure 38   (a) High positive correlation   (b) High negative correlation

When there is high positive correlation, r is close to +1, and when there is high negative correlation, r is close to –1.

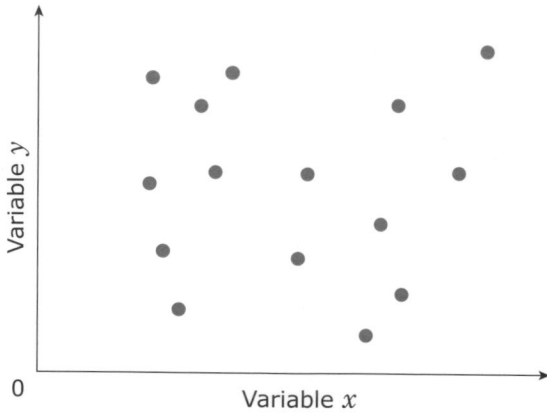

Figure 39 No correlation (r = 0)

Because you check for a correlation only when you think one may exist, it is actually very rare to find pairs of variables with zero correlation. However, if variables have very weak correlation (a correlation coefficient near 0), this means that there is no clear tendency for a variable to move in one direction (up or down) with changes in the other variable. With perfect, that is, +1 or −1, correlation, all the variation in the dependent variable can be explained by the variation in the independent variable.

Mathematically, the amount of association between two variables can be calculated by computing the 'correlation coefficient' using a number of alternative formulae, each of which will produce the same answer. The following formula will be used:

$$r = \frac{n\sum xy - \sum x \sum y}{\sqrt{\left[n\sum x^2 - \left(\sum x\right)^2\right]\left[n\sum y^2 - \left(\sum y\right)^2\right]}}$$

Note that in your examination you may be asked to calculate the correlation coefficient. However, in a work situation it can be calculated using a spreadsheet package.

Let us calculate the correlation coefficient using the age and height figures presented earlier in this section.

	Age	Height			
	x	y	xy	x^2	y^2
	2	75	150	4	5,625
	3	81	243	9	6,561
	4	96	384	16	9,216
	4	102	408	16	10,404
	5	90	450	25	8,100
	5	120	600	25	14,400
	6	106	636	36	11,236
	6	122	732	36	14,884
Totals	35	792	3,603	167	80,426
	Σx	Σy	Σxy	Σx^2	Σy^2

$$r = \frac{8(3{,}603) - (35)(792)}{\sqrt{[8(167) - (35)^2]\,[8(80{,}426) - (792)^2]}} = +0.825$$

Scientific calculator reminder

Enter

⌨ 8 (3,603) – (35) (792) ▼ √ (8 (167) – (35) x^2))
(8 (80,426) – (792) x^2)) =

The value of +0.825 shows that there was a strong positive correlation. This value is quite close to +1, so it is not surprising that the scatter diagram (Figure 36) showed the points fairly close together.

In essence, information about how close the observations are to lying on a straight line is captured in one number from –1 to +1.

Correlation is a necessary feature of a causal relationship, but it is *not* sufficient proof that a causal relationship exists. Correlation does not mean the same as causation. It is up to the person using the information to determine why the relationship exists. Just because two variables appear connected (using the data available) does not necessarily mean that one *caused* the other. The stronger the correlation, the better the evidence that there is a real link between the two, but it is seldom certain that this is the case: something else may be causing it.

There are instances when two variables may show a strong correlation, but the movement in one variable does not cause the movement in the other. This is known as **spurious correlation**. Examples might be an increase in mobile phone purchases with an increase in alcohol consumption, and an increase in the UK birth rate with a growth in the stork population.

3.3 Coefficient of determination (r^2)

Unless the correlation coefficient is +1 or –1, its precise meaning may be unclear. How much of the change in y can be explained by a change in x is indicated by the **coefficient of determination**, which is the square of the correlation coefficient.

For the age and height example, the correlation coefficient was found to be +0.825. The coefficient of determination (known as r squared) is therefore $0.825^2 = 0.68$. This shows that 68% of the variations in height can be explained by age.

The result of this statistical analysis indicates either a stronger or weaker likelihood of there being a connection between the two variables. To be certain, you need to discover the mechanism that links the two variables, for example, in the case of a telephone bill, the relationship between the number of call minutes and the amount charged.

Activity 3.1 ....

If age explains only 68% of the changes in height, what do you think might explain the other 32% of the changes in height?

Feedback ....

The remaining 32% of the changes in height is due to other factors, possibly, environment, genetics, diet, etc.

Strong correlation (i.e., close to +1 or −1) may give evidence of a connection between the variables, but it still requires other evidence to decide the significance to be placed on the result.

3.4 The scatter graph method

While correlation shows whether there is a relationship between variables and the strength of that relationship, it does not give a means of forecasting the future value of the dependent variable. If, however, a linear relationship between the two variables is assumed, the variables can be plotted on a scatter graph and a line of best fit determined 'by eye'. That line can then be used, with caution, as the basis for forecasting the dependent variable.

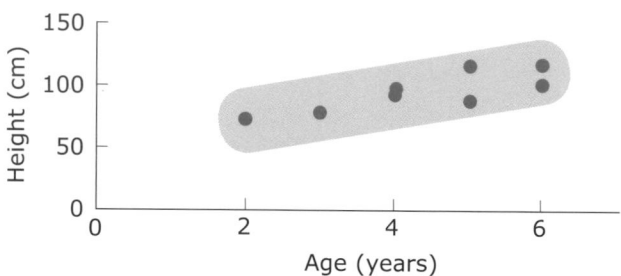

Figure 40   Scatter graph indicating positive correlation

In the graph above, the line of best fit would be drawn somewhere within the marked area. However, different people would draw the line slightly differently from each other. This line of best fit, once drawn, may be used to predict the likely height of children by reading off the values from the graph. It must not be assumed that the slope of the line will continue in the same way, should it be extended, as children grow at differing rates as they get older, and there is a difference between the rate of growth of girls and that of boys. Reading off values within the range shown by the points plotted on the scatter graph is called **interpolation**; extending the line of the graph beyond the known values of *x* and *y* is called **extrapolation**.

3.5 Regression analysis – the least squares method

The line of best fit is also known as the regression line, the least squares fit line and the trend line.

The line of best fit obtained by using the scatter graph method above is good enough for practical purposes such as illustrating data or making simple predictions. It is not, however, reliable, as one person may plot the line in one way and another in a slightly different way, perhaps, to support a particular argument (bias).

A more accurate and reliable way of calculating a line of best fit is to use the least squares method to produce a **regression line**.

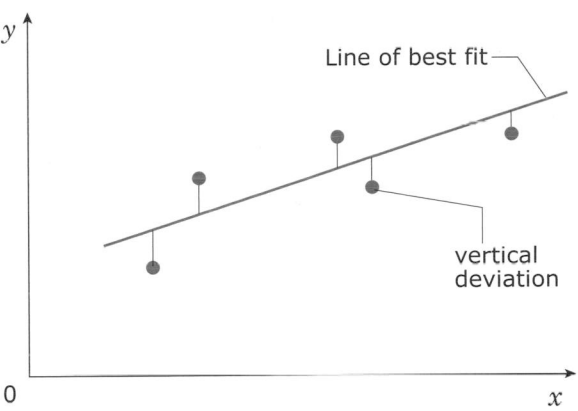

Figure 41 Line of best fit

Linear regression analyses a set of points and fits the best straight line to these. (Note, however, that the correlation coefficient should always be calculated to see how good the association is between the variables.)

Linear regression:

- measures the vertical distances of each point from this line
- finds the sum of the squares of distances and minimises it.

Using the equation of a straight line:

$$y = a + bx$$

where

a and b are constants

a represents the fixed element, the intercept of the line on the vertical axis

b represents the slope of the line

In Section 2.2.2 on line graphs, the rental cost a in the telephone bill example was known. However, in general, it is necessary to solve two simultaneous equations to find a and b. (Please refer back to Session 1 if you have difficulty in solving simultaneous equations.) It is the same with regression lines.

To find the values of a and b it is necessary to solve two equations:

Equation 1 $\sum y = an + b \sum x$ where n = the number of pairs of figures.

Equation 2 $\sum xy = a \sum x + b \sum x^2$

These equations look worse than they really are. The first equation is very similar to the equation for a straight line $y = a + bx$, and the second equation $\sum xy = a \sum x + b \sum x^2$ is similar to the first but n is replaced by $\sum$ and each $\sum$ is followed by an x.

Consider the following example. To a certain extent, sales made will depend on price, so price is the independent variable x and quantity sold the dependent variable y.

Period	1	2	3	4	5	6	7	8	9	10
Price (£) x	7.5	7.0	6.5	6.0	6.0	5.5	5.0	5.0	5.5	6.0
Sales ('000) y	5	10	15	20	25	45	50	60	45	65

Looking at Equations 1 and 2, $\sum x$, $\sum y$, $\sum xy$ and $\sum x^2$ need to be calculated.

x	y	xy	x^2
7.5	5	37.5	56.25
7.0	10	70	49
6.5	15	97.5	42.25
6.0	20	120	36
6.0	25	150	36
5.5	45	247.5	30.25
5.0	50	250	25
5.0	60	300	25
5.5	45	247.5	30.25
6.0	65	390	36
60.0	340	1,910	366
Σx	Σy	Σxy	Σx^2

Putting this data into the two equations:

$$\sum y = an + b \sum x \text{ becomes } 340 = a \times 10 + b \times 60$$

$$\sum xy = a \sum x + b \sum x^2 \text{ becomes } 1{,}910 = a \times 60 + b \times 366$$

The two equations are thus:

$$340 = 10a + 60b \qquad \text{(equation 1)}$$

$$1{,}910 = 60a + 366b \qquad \text{(equation 2)}$$

To solve the equations, multiply equation 1 by 6 so that both equations have 60a in them, and deduct equation 2 from the result:

$$2{,}040 = 60a + 360b$$

$$1{,}910 = 60a + 366b$$

$$130 = -6b$$

Therefore $b = -21.67$

Putting $b = -21.67$ into equation 1 gives: $340 = 10a - 21.67 \times 60$ which is $340 = 10a - 1{,}300$. Adding 1,300 to both sides gives $1{,}640 = 10a$.

Therefore $a = 164$.

If you are unsure of how to solve simultaneous equations please refer back to Section 1.11. If you are still unhappy with this area, you can derive b from the following two formulae:

$$a = \frac{\sum y - b \sum x}{n}$$

where

x and y are related variables

x is the independent variable

y is the dependent variable

a is the intercept of the line of the vertical axis

b is the gradient of the line

$$\text{so } a = \frac{340 - b \times 60}{10}$$

$$b = \frac{n\sum xy - \sum x \sum y}{n\sum x^2 - \left(\sum x\right)^2}$$

$$\text{so } b = \frac{10(1,910) - 60(340)}{10(366) - (60)^2} = \frac{19,100 - 20,400}{3,660 - 3,600} = \frac{-1,300}{60} = -21.67$$

Putting $b = -21.67$ into the formula for a gives:

$$a = \frac{\sum y - b\sum x}{n} = \frac{340 - (-21.67)60}{10} = \frac{340 - (-1300.2)}{10}$$

$$= \frac{1,640.2}{10} = 164 \text{ (rounded)}$$

The regression line $y = a + bx$ is therefore:

$$y = 164 - 21.67x$$

This line could now be drawn on a scatter graph and the predicted demand for the product read off. However, in practice, the formula $y = 164 - 21.67x$ is used. So if the price were set at £3, predicted sales would be 98,990 (remember the sales were expressed in thousands so the 98.99 must be multiplied by 1,000).

$y = 164 - 21.67 \times 3 = 98.99$ and $98.99 \times 1,000$ is 98,990.

Limitations

While least squares regression provides a more reliable estimate of a line of best fit than the scatter graph method, it has a number of limitations, as follows.

- A linear relationship between two variables is assumed to exist, whereas a non linear relationship may exist.

- Occurrences in the past are assumed to provide a reliable guide to the future. This may not be the case due to external factors or internal factors. External factors may be changes in consumer preferences; changes in competitor offerings; the economy being in recession; a period of high inflation, etc. Internal factors may include the organisation introducing new, more efficient equipment, reducing the labour time or using new production methods.

- It is assumed that the value of one variable can be predicted or estimated from the value of the other. However, in practice, one variable may be influenced by a number of other variables.

3.6 Forecasting

All businesses need to plan ahead. **Forecasting** (predicting future outcomes) using quantitative techniques helps in this process.

The above techniques will not necessarily provide accurate forecasts. However, the information they provide will be better than relying on guesswork. They do not remove uncertainty about the future, but they do help management to take account of currently known facts.

- Scatter graphs can be used for making simple predictions, although there is no precision as to where the line of best fit actually is.

- The least squares regression analysis offers accuracy and reliability provided that forecasts are made within the data range (interpolation). If, however, the regression line is extended beyond the known points (extrapolation), the line may not give a reliable estimate, as the relationship between x and y may not persist beyond the points plotted. For example, when looking at sales, after a certain volume of sales the market may become saturated and sales would not increase in response to a price reduction, while immediately prior to that point the increase in sales would slow.

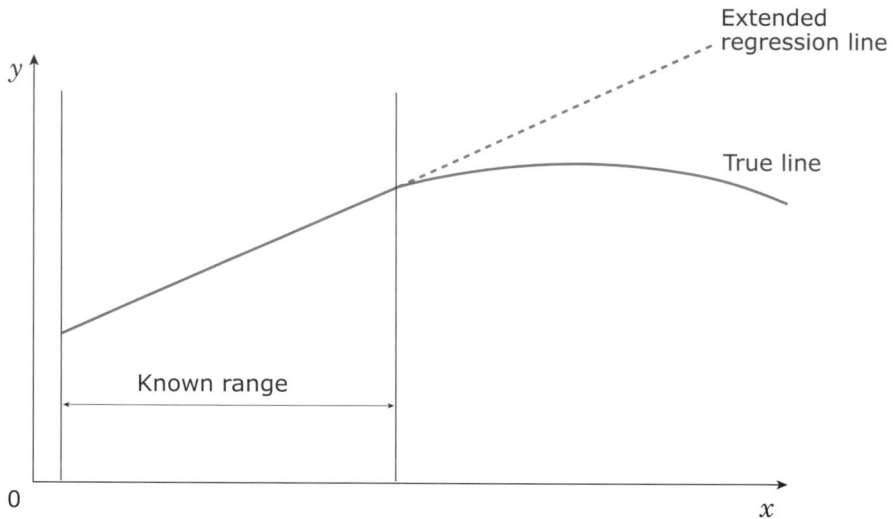

Figure 42   Extending the regression line

Also, if circumstances change substantially, such as a change occurring in the company's marketing strategy, a new regression line would need to be drawn using data obtained after the change. If a straight-line relationship no longer applies, then straight-line regression could not continue to be used in forecasting.

In Section 2.2.3, you saw how time series graphs show patterns of ups and downs in the data from one month to the next. A number of variables, including sales, costs, profit, advertising, etc., may rise, fall or stay the same over time. **Time series analysis** is a technique used in forecasting to adjust for any seasonal variations and to extrapolate the underlying trend.

3.7 Time series analysis

There may be several time-related factors causing the sales volume to vary. These variations may be due to four different components, as outlined below.

1   **Seasonal variations** – regular repeating changes in demand in periods of less than one year. For example, domestic energy consumption will be higher in winter months than in summer months, while the demand for garden furniture will be higher in summer months.

2   **Long-term trend** – hopefully, the underlying **trend** in sales volume will be upwards.

3   **Cyclical variations** – the periodic rise and fall of the whole data series over a number of years, possibly due to the economy going through the classic boom/bust cycle every five to ten years.

4   **Random variations** – the remaining variations that cannot be attributed to 1 to 3 above, for example, irregularities in shop takings caused by snow, flooding or machine breakdown.

The following sales revenue data have been collected over five years.

Year	Quarter 1	Quarter 2	Quarter 3	Quarter 4
	£'000	£'000	£'000	£'000
1	73	99	93	126
2	81	114	108	148
3	91	121	117	154
4	106	131	135	175
5	134	149		

The following figure shows the data on a time series graph:

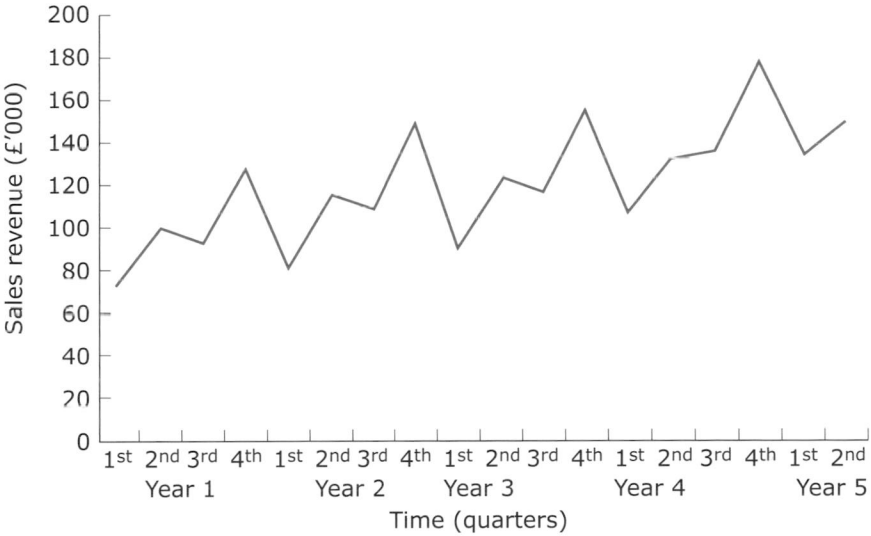

Figure 43   Time series graph showing sales revenue by quarter for four and a half years

The objective of time series analysis is to break down the pattern shown by the recorded values into characteristic variations (defined above) and project each characteristic into the future. They can then be recombined to arrive at a forecast.

3.7.1   Seasonal variation

Looking at the time series graph, the first thing that may strike you is that in each year there is a peak in the fourth quarter. This indicates a seasonal variation. In order to use the data for forecasting, this seasonal variation must be removed.

Seasonal nature of sales

Note that random variations (R) are generally ignored, as they are usually both small and unpredictable.

The seasonal variation can be removed using either of two methods.

- The **additive method** is where

  actual sales (A) = trend (T) + seasonal variation (S) + random variations (R)

  It assumes that the size of the seasonal variation is not affected by the size of the trend figures. To estimate the seasonal variation (S) using this method, deduct the trend (T) from the actual sales (A), so $S = A - T$. We ignore R since by definition R cannot be predicted.

- The **multiplicative method** (also known as the proportional method) is where

  actual sales (A) = trend (T) × seasonal variation (S) × random variation (R)

  This method assumes that the size of the seasonal variation is proportional to the size of the trend. When using this method, divide the actual sales by the trend, so $S = A/T$.

While the calculations involved in the additive method are easier than those in the multiplicative method, the multiplicative method will usually give more reliable results. Whichever method is used, the basic trend must be found first.

Identifying the trend

To identify the trend line calculate a four quarter moving average (using a moving total), starting with the sales revenue data for the first four quarters and then progressively replace the oldest quarter's result with the next quarter's result. This is illustrated in Table 3.1.

Add up the first four quarters and take the average:

$$\frac{73 + 99 + 93 + 126}{4} = \frac{391}{4} = 97.75$$

Then add up quarters 2 to 5 and take the average:

$$\frac{99 + 93 + 126 + 81}{4} = \frac{399}{4} = 99.75$$

Then add up quarters 3 to 6, and so on.

Table 3.1 Calculation of four quarter moving average

Year	Quarter	Sales	4 quarter moving total	4 quarter moving average
		£'000	£'000	£'000
1	1	73		
	2	99		
			391	97.75
	3	93		
			399	99.75
	4	126		
			414	103.50
2	1	81		
			429	107.25
	2	114		
			451	112.75
	3	108		
	4	148		

When using a spreadsheet, no rounding of the data would take place. When doing the calculation manually, though, it is tempting to round the data to, say, one decimal place, but it is better not to do so.

As the first average is a four quarter result, it cannot be compared directly with the results from any one quarter (the first average falls between the second and third quarters, and so on). This is done in order to find the distance of the actual data from the trend, that is, the seasonal variation. In order to compare the average results with the actual results, they must be 'centred'. This means taking the average of each adjacent pair of averages. Now, instead of being between the actual quarter results, they are lined up alongside them as shown in the right-hand column of Table 3.2.

Table 3.2 Calculation of centred four quarter moving average

Year	Quarter	Actual sales (A)	4 quarter moving total	4 quarter moving average	Trend (T) (also known as centred 4 quarter moving average)
		£'000	£'000	£'000	£'000
1	1	73			
	2	99			
			391	97.75	
	3	93			98.750
			399	99.75	
	4	126			101.625
			414	103.50	
2	1	81			105.375
			429	107.25	
	2	114			110.000
			451	112.75	
	3	108			

Now that the trend has been identified, the data can be used to calculate the seasonal variation.

Calculating the seasonal variation using the additive method

The additive method is where

$$\text{actual sales } (A) = \text{basic trend } (T) + \text{seasonal variation } (S) + \text{random variations } (R)$$

To estimate the seasonal variation using this method the trend is deducted from the actual sales, so $S = A - T$. (R is ignored.)

In the additive method the seasonal variation, that is, the seasonal trend, can be identified by comparing each centred four quarter average (the basic trend line) with each actual data value as:

$$\text{actual sales revenue } (A) = \text{basic trend } (T) \pm \text{seasonal variation } (S)$$

The calculations are given in Table 3.3.

Please note that this table contains the same information as Table 3.2 with seasonal variation added.

Table 3.3 Calculation of seasonal variation

Year	Quarter	Actual sales (A)	4 quarter moving total	4 quarter moving average	Trend (T) (centred 4 quarter moving average)	Seasonal variation (A − T)
		£'000	£'000	£'000	£'000	£'000
1	1	73				
	2	99				
			391	97.75		
	3	93			98.750	(5.750)
			399	99.75		
	4	126			101.625	24.375
			414	103.50		
2	1	81			105.375	(24.375)
			429	107.25		
	2	114			110.000	4.000
			451	112.75		
	3	108				

If this analysis is carried out for the entire data set, the results shown in Table 3.4 are obtained.

Table 3.4 Trend and seasonal variation for all the data

Year	Quarter	Actual sales (A)	Trend (T) (centred 4 quarter moving average)	Seasonal variation (A − T)
		£'000	£'000	£'000
1	1	73		
	2	99		
	3	93	98.750	(5.750)
	4	126	101.625	24.375
2	1	81	105.375	(24.375)
	2	114	110.000	4.000
	3	108	114.000	(6.000)
	4	148	116.125	31.875
3	1	91	118.125	(27.125)
	2	121	120.000	1.000
	3	117	122.625	(5.625)
	4	154	125.750	28.250
4	1	106	129.250	(23.250)
	2	131	134.125	(3.125)
	3	135	140.250	(5.250)
	4	175	146.000	29.000
5	1	134		
	2	149		

The fact that the adjustments for quarter 3 sales are not the same in years 1, 2, 3 and onwards indicates that the data contain random variations. To remove these random variations the variations for each quarter can be tabulated and averaged.

Table 3.5 Calculation of average seasonal variation

Year	Quarter 1	Quarter 2	Quarter 3	Quarter 4
	£'000	£'000	£'000	£'000
1			(5.750)	24.375
2	(24.375)	4.000	(6.000)	31.875
3	(27.125)	1.000	(5.625)	28.250
4	(23.250)	(3.125)	(5.250)	29.000
Total	(74.750)	1.875	(22.625)	113.500
Average seasonal variation (*(24.917)=(74.750) divided by 3 as there are 3 quarters)	*(24.917)	0.625	(5.656)	28.375
Corrected average	(24.524)	1.018	(5.263)	28.768

The average seasonal variations should add up to zero. Any difference can be averaged over the four quarters. In this case the difference is −1.573, so 0.393 could be added to each quarter. So the set of average seasonal variations that should apply to any year are now known.

Calculating the seasonal variation using the multiplicative method

The multiplicative method is where

actual sales (A) = trend (T) × seasonal variation (S)
× random variation (R)

We ignore random variation (R) since by definition R cannot be predicted. Ignoring (R), the formula can be rearranged, so seasonally adjusted sales or trend (T) = the actual sales (A) divided by the seasonal component (S).

Table 3.6   Trend and seasonal variation for all the data

Year	Quarter	Sales (A)	Trend (T) (centred 4 quarter moving average)	Seasonal variation (A/T)
		£'000	£'000	
1	1	73		
	2	99		
	3	93	98.750	0.942
	4	126	101.625	1.240
2	1	81	105.375	0.769
	2	114	110.000	1.036
	3	108	114.000	0.947
	4	148	116.125	1.274
3	1	91	118.125	0.770
	2	121	120.000	1.008
	3	117	122.625	0.954
	4	154	125.750	1.225
4	1	106	129.250	0.820
	2	131	134.125	0.977
	3	135	140.250	0.963
	4	175	146.000	1.199
5	1	134		
	2	149		

The fact that the adjustments for quarter 1 sales are not the same in years 2, 3, 4 and onwards indicates that the data contain random variations. To remove these random variations, the variations for each quarter can be tabulated and averaged.

The sum of these averages should be 4 (i.e., one per quarter as there are four quarters). If, as in this case, the sum of the differences does not sum to 4, the averages can be corrected by adding one-quarter of the difference to each of the quarters.

Table 3.7   Calculation of average seasonal variation

Year	Quarter 1	Quarter 2	Quarter 3	Quarter 4
1			0.942	1.240
2	0.769	1.036	0.947	1.274
3	0.770	1.008	0.954	1.225
4	0.820	0.977	0.963	1.199
Total	2.359	3.021	3.806	4.938
Average seasonal variation (* 0.786 = 2.359 divided by 3 as there are 3 quarters)	*0.786	1.007	0.952	1.235
Corrected average	0.791	1.012	0.957	1.240

The sum of the averages is 3.980, the total error is therefore +0.020 (4 – 3.980), so 0.005 (one quarter of 0.020) is added to each quarter to give the corrected average. Note the corrected average now adds up to 4.000 (as there are four quarters).

3.7.2 Basic trend

The following graph shows the actual sales and the basic trend.

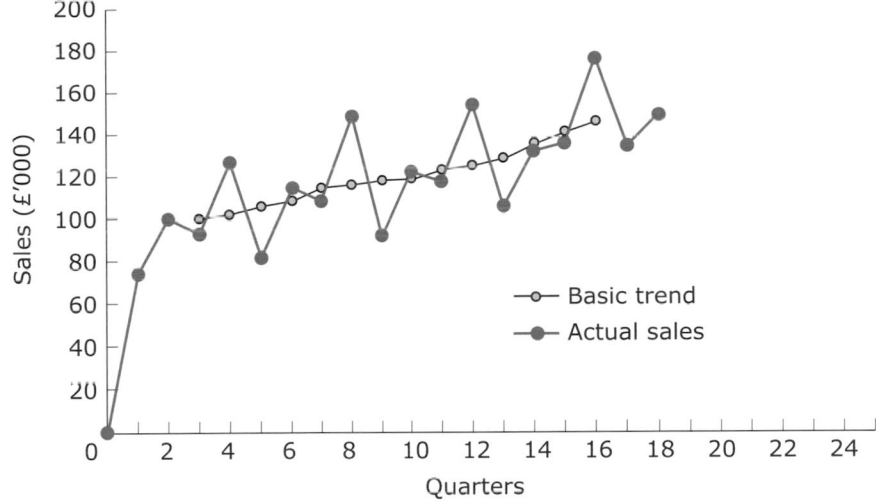

Figure 44   Actual sales and basic trend (data from Table 3.4)

Having isolated the average seasonal variations, it is now possible to remove these variations. This is known as **de-seasonalising** the original data. These seasonally adjusted data will still include basic trend, cyclical and random movements.

However, if it is assumed that the cyclical and random factors are not significant, the future sales figures can be forecast by extrapolating the basic trend line determined in Table 3.4 (and in Table 3.6) with adjustment for the seasonal variation.

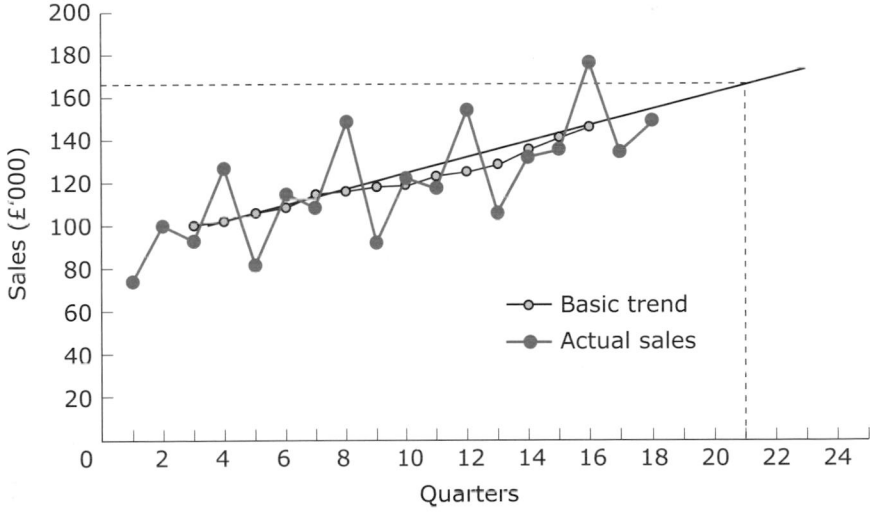

Figure 45   Extrapolation of the basic trend line

Reading the twenty-first quarter extrapolated trend from the above graph shows that the forecast sales revenue is around £163,000 or £164,000. However, the method preferred by many is to calculate the figure. For example, if an accountant wished to predict the sales revenue for the first quarter of year 6 (the twenty-first quarter), he/she would take the last basic trend reading of £146,000 (shown in Tables 3.4 and 3.6), deduct the first basic trend reading (£98,750) and divide the result (£47,250) by the number of movements in the basic trend (13) to arrive at the average quarterly rise (£3,634.62). For the twenty-first quarter forecast, the average quarterly rise (£3,634.62) is multiplied by the number of quarters from the last basic trend figure to the twenty-first quarter (5) and the result £18,173 is added to the last basic trend figure (£146,000).

$$\text{So } £146{,}000 + \left(\frac{£146{,}000 - £98{,}750}{13} \times 5 \right) = £146{,}000 + £18{,}173$$
$$= £164{,}173.$$

All that has to be done now (assuming random variations are negligible) is to adjust for the first quarter seasonal variation.

Using the additive methods, this is £164,173 – £24,524 = £139,649.

Using the multiplicative method, this is £164,173 × 0.791 = £129,861.

A word of warning: the projecting of the trend line (extrapolation) is made on the assumption that the trend will continue. Any unforeseen circumstances may invalidate this assumption.

Of course, the further ahead the forecasting, the less reliable it will be, as it is based upon the assumption that the basic trend will continue.

Summary

This session looked at ways to describe the types of association that can exist between variables. Correlation describes how variables move together, but does not imply causality. Regression analysis was used to quantify the relationship between two variables, and you saw that it can be used for forecasting and is generally reliable when predictions are the result of interpolation. Where, however, extrapolation is used, reliability is far from certain. The session then considered the fact that not all variables can be linked by a straight line, as summarised data may show a trend masked by seasonal effects. Time series analysis was used to break down the data pattern into characteristic variations and project each characteristic into the future. These projections can then be re-combined to arrive at a forecast. Session 4 introduces you to various techniques that can be used to provide information for decision making where there is risk and uncertainty.

SESSION **4 Risk and uncertainty in management decision making**

Introduction

Upon completion of Session 4, you are expected to be able to:

- explain what is meant by probability
- express probabilities in terms of percentages, proportions, fractions and decimals
- demonstrate the addition and multiplication rules of probability
- use expected values in simple decision making situations
- explain the limitations of expected value techniques
- understand the properties of the normal distribution curve
- calculate probabilities from the normal distribution curve
- understand and explain the concept of risk and uncertainty in the context of management decision making.

This session looks at various techniques that can be used to provide management information to help in decision making where there is risk or uncertainty. In every day speech, risk and uncertainty are taken as one and the same. In business decision making situations, however, it is important to recognise the difference.

Risk occurs when there is more than one possible outcome and it is possible to assign probabilities to these possible outcomes. In looking at risk, the rules of probability are examined to consider various different situations where risk exists, so that the risk can be quantified in terms of mathematical probabilities. Probabilities can be used to help anticipate the future, and make decisions that help to cope with risk. The normal distribution curve can also help to assess whether a result could reasonably be expected to occur or whether it is so unlikely that it must be regarded as significant.

There is **uncertainty** when a number of different outcomes is possible, but it is *not* possible to assign probabilities to these outcomes. Three quantitative approaches to uncertainty, namely the Maximax, Maximin and Minimax Regret decision making rules, are discussed.

4.1 Probability

Probability refers to the chance of something happening. Probability theory enables the likelihood of an event to be measured on a scale of impossible (zero probability) to certain (100% probability), in the range 0 to 1, as a fraction or a decimal.

Probability	Impossible	Evens (equally likely)	Certain
As a percentage	0%	50%	100%
As a number from 0 to 1	0	0.5	1.00
In terms of a fraction	0	$\frac{1}{2}$	1

If there is a 0.7 probability of winning a tender, this means that there is a 70% chance or a $\frac{7}{10}$ chance of winning. Conversely, there is a (1.00 − 0.7) = 0.3 or 30% chance that a bid will be unsuccessful. The closer to 0 the probability of success, the more unlikely it is that the event will happen. The closer to 1 the probability lies, the more likely it is that the event will happen.

4.1.1   Law of proportions

Whenever an action can have more than one result, the probability of any result occurring in a single test is the proportion which that particular result bears to all possible results.

For example:

- The probability of rolling a die and obtaining a number 5 is $\frac{1}{6}$, as there is only one 5 on the die and six numbers altogether, all equally likely to be obtained if the die is fair.

- The probability of obtaining an even number is $\frac{3}{6}$ or 50–50, as you could throw a 2, 4 or 6. The probability of a number less than seven is $\frac{6}{6}$ or 1.00, as all the possible numbers are below seven.

Activity 4.1 ··

If you threw two dice, what is the probability that the numbers obtained will add up to seven?

Feedback ··

The answer is 0.16666, which can be rounded to 0.17.

Every time you throw a die, it can give you any one of six numbers. Therefore if you throw two dice there are 36 possible combinations (6 × 6 = 36). When you throw a die and it shows a 4, and then you throw the second die there are six possible numbers that may be shown by the second die. For each number shown on the first die, any one of six numbers may be shown on the second die. Only the following combinations give seven:

1 and 6   2 and 5   3 and 4   4 and 3   5 and 2   6 and 1

Therefore the probability is that, from the 36 combinations, six will produce a total of seven, or 6/36 which equals 0.1666 which is 0.17 when rounded to 2 d.p.

Activity 4.2 ··

A quality control inspection revealed that, of 140 units checked at random, 42 had a fault.

(a) State as a fraction in its simplest form the probability of any one of the units having a fault.

(b) The line produces 900 units a week. Using the figure calculated in part (a), calculate how many units could be expected to be faulty.

Feedback ··

(a) $\frac{42}{140}$ (the top and bottom are divisible by 7) $= \frac{6}{20} = \frac{3}{10}$

(b) $900 \times \frac{3}{10} = 270$

4.1.2 Combined events

To find the probability of a combined event, that is, where two or more events can happen, it is important to be clear about whether either event can happen, but not necessarily at the same time as the other, or whether one event occurring prevents the other. These possible outcomes fall into different types that can be described as OR and AND.

Such situations can be represented using **Venn diagrams**. A rectangle represents the universe (the complete set of outcomes that could occur). Within the rectangle, circles are used to represent events.

Addition (OR) law for mutually exclusive events

Events are said to be mutually exclusive if the occurrence of one means that the other cannot occur.

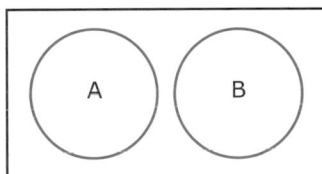

Figure 46   Venn diagram for mutually exclusive events

The circles for A and B do not overlap, as A and B have nothing in common.

The addition (OR) law is used to calculate the probability of two or more mutually exclusive events. For example, the probability of throwing a 2 OR a 5 with a single throw of a die is therefore:

$$P(\text{throwing a 2}) = \frac{1}{6}$$

$$P(\text{throwing a 5}) = \frac{1}{6}$$

$$P(\text{throwing a 2 or a 5}) = \frac{1}{6} + \frac{1}{6} = \frac{2}{6} = \frac{1}{3}$$

Here is another example. A company has organised its annual staff outing to the seaside but is concerned about the weather. The weather reports give a $\frac{1}{5}$ chance of rain and a $\frac{2}{5}$ chance of an overcast day with no rain. What is the probability that the employees will have a sunny day?

$$P(\text{overcast or raining, i.e., not sunny})$$

$$= \frac{1}{5} + \frac{2}{5} = \frac{3}{5} = \frac{6}{10} = 0.6 \text{ (or 60\%)}$$

$$P(\text{sunny}) = 1.00 - 0.6 = 0.4 \text{ (or 40\%)}$$

Multiplication (AND) law for non-mutually exclusive events

When events can happen at the same time, they are said to be non-mutually exclusive. To find this combined probability, the probabilities of each event are multiplied.

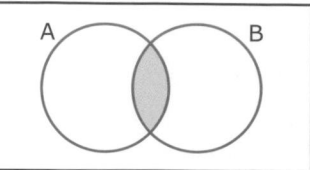

Figure 47   Venn diagram for non-mutually exclusive events

The circles for A and B overlap, as both events can occur at the same time.

The multiplication (AND) law is used to calculate the probability of combined events. For example, the probability of throwing a 2 AND a 5 with two consecutive throws of a die is therefore:

$$P(\text{throwing a 2}) = \frac{1}{6}$$

$$P(\text{throwing a 5}) = \frac{1}{6}$$

$$P(\text{throwing a 2 and a 5}) = \frac{1}{6} \times \frac{1}{6} = \frac{1}{36}$$

Here is another example. A company is working on developing two new products. It estimates there is a $\frac{1}{5}$ chance of product A being successfully developed and a $\frac{3}{5}$ chance of product B being successfully developed. There are no inter-relationships between the two products. The chance of both products being successfully developed is:

$$P(\text{A successfully developed}) = \frac{1}{5}$$

$$P(\text{B successfully developed}) = \frac{3}{5}$$

$$P(\text{A and B successfully developed}) = \frac{1}{5} \times \frac{3}{5} = \frac{3}{25} = \frac{6}{50} = \frac{12}{100}$$

$$= 0.12 \text{ (or a 12\% chance)}$$

'Well, the forecast was a 60% chance of rain, so I bought 60% of an umbrella.'

Activity 4.3 ....

Think of an example of a problem that would require the use of each law.

(a) Law of proportions

(b) Addition (OR) law

(c) Multiplication (AND) law

Feedback ....

(a) Law of proportions

Whenever any action can have more than one result, the probability of any result occurring, in a single test, is the proportion which that particular result bears to all possible results.

An example could be throwing a die and having a $\frac{1}{6}$ chance of it showing a 3.

(b) Addition (OR) law

Whenever any action can have more than one result, provided that all possible results are mutually exclusive, the probability of alternative results occurring in a single test will be the sum of their individual probabilities.

An example could be throwing a die where there is a $\frac{1}{6}$ chance of it showing a 3 and a $\frac{1}{6}$ chance of it showing a 4. The probability of throwing either a 3 or a 4 is therefore:

$$P(\text{throwing 3}) = \frac{1}{6}$$

$$P(\text{throwing 4}) = \frac{1}{6}$$

$$P(\text{throwing 3 or 4}) = \frac{1}{6} + \frac{1}{6} - \frac{1}{3}$$

(c) Multiplication (AND) law

Whenever any action can have more than one result, the probability of getting any particular combination in a fixed order from two or more independent tests (consecutive or simultaneous) will be the product of their individual probabilities.

An example could be throwing a die twice where there is a $\frac{1}{6}$ chance of it showing a 3 the first time and a $\frac{1}{6}$ chance of it showing a 3 the second time as well. The probability of obtaining two 3s in a row is therefore:

$$P(\text{throwing 3 and 3}) = \frac{1}{6} \times \frac{1}{6} = \frac{1}{36}$$

4.1.3   Conditional probability

Conditional probability is the probability that one event will occur given that another event has already occurred.

The director of Décor Limited is considering whether a contract for painting the outside of a building can be completed on time and within budget. He has identified three factors:

(a) the probability of bad weather

(b) the likelihood of remedial work being required

(c) whether the work can be finished without having to pay overtime.

A **probability tree** is a tree-like diagram with a series of branches showing from left to right the alternative probabilities of different consecutive events. Each junction between branches, shown as a circle, represents an alternative (OR event) and is known as a chance node.

The probability of the event occurring at the chance node is written along each branch.

Probabilities may be written as fractions or as decimals. Note that the probabilities at each chance node must add up to 1. For example, in Figure 48, the probabilities on the branches coming out of the first chance node are 0.5, 0.2 and 0.3, which sum to 1.

The overall probability of a result represented by an individual branch occurring (AND event) is found by multiplying together the probabilities of all the branches leading back to the start of the tree. For example, in Figure 48, the probability of the upper right-hand branch is found by multiplying 0.7 by 0.5 to give 0.35 or 35%.

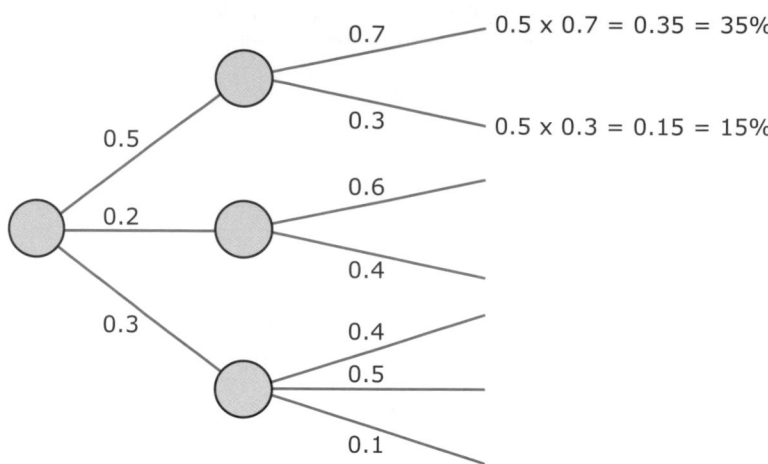

Figure 48   Probability tree showing the calculation of outcomes arising from the first main branch

Example

An accountant is driving from the north of Paris via the A1 and the A5 to an important meeting in the south. There is a $\frac{1}{10}$ chance of being delayed on the A1 motorway and a $\frac{1}{5}$ chance of being delayed on the A5 motorway. What is the probability that the accountant will be delayed at some point on the journey?

Figure 49 shows the situation.

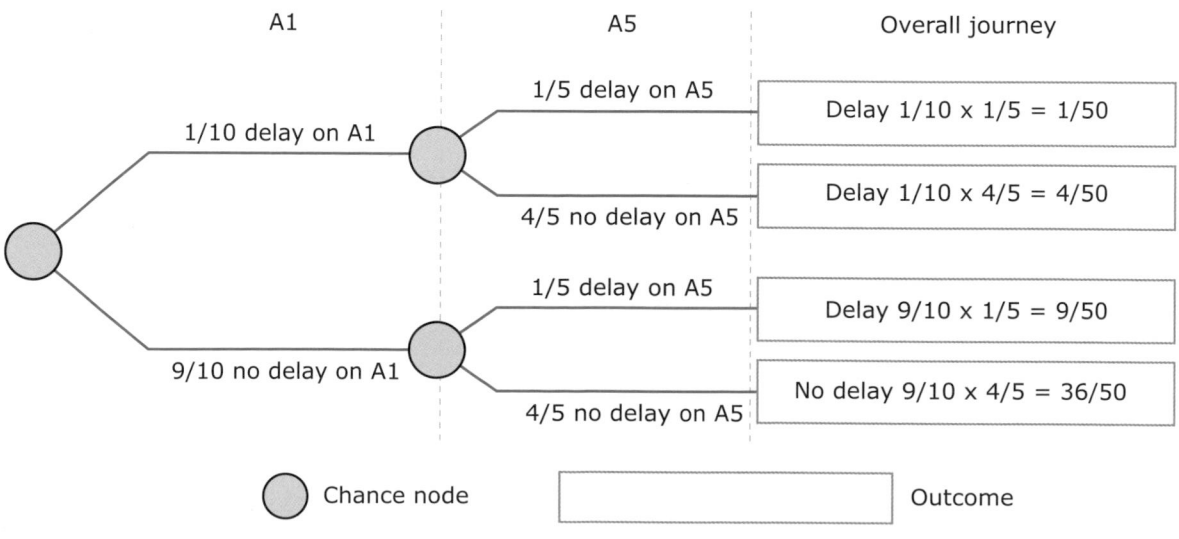

Figure 49   Probability tree

The AND events are put along the branches of the tree and the probabilities of each branch are found by multiplying along the branches. Each OR event is represented by a separate branch and therefore, to find the total probability that the accountant will be delayed at some point on the journey, the probabilities of each branch must be added.

The probability of being delayed is:

$$\frac{1}{50} + \frac{4}{50} + \frac{9}{50} = \frac{14}{50} = \frac{28}{100} = 28\%$$

Notice that only one branch has no delay along it and the probability of no delay is:

$$\frac{36}{50} = \frac{72}{100} = 72\%$$

You will not be surprised that the two probabilities total 100%, because the accountant can only be delayed (28%) or not delayed (72%).

The rules of using probability trees can be summarised as follows.

- The probabilities at each chance node must add up to one.

- Multiply probabilities along branches.

- Add probabilities between branches.

4.1.4   Decision trees

Decision trees are diagrams which show the choices available and the likely outcomes of each choice. They:

- clearly set out the problem so that options can be considered

- show all the possible consequences of a decision to be analysed

- provide a framework in which to quantify the values of outcomes and the probabilities of achieving each outcome

- help the decision maker to make the best decision based on available information and best estimates.

Decision trees are an extension of probability trees. However, rather than just having chance nodes they also have decision nodes, which are represented by a square. Branches at each split-off point will be represented by either (a) a circle (chance node) representing the point that this possibility or that possibility could happen or (b) by a square (decision node) representing the point at which a decision should be made.

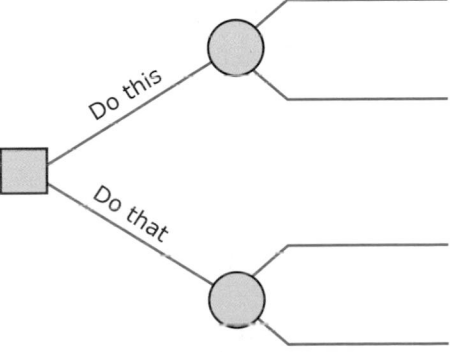

Figure 50   Decision tree

Activity 4.4

A department has 30 workers of whom 15 are skilled, 10 are semi-skilled and 5 are manual labourers. If two workers are randomly selected to represent the department on a works council, use a decision tree to determine the probability that they will both be of the same grade.

The first node will be a decision node, which is represented by a square.

Feedback

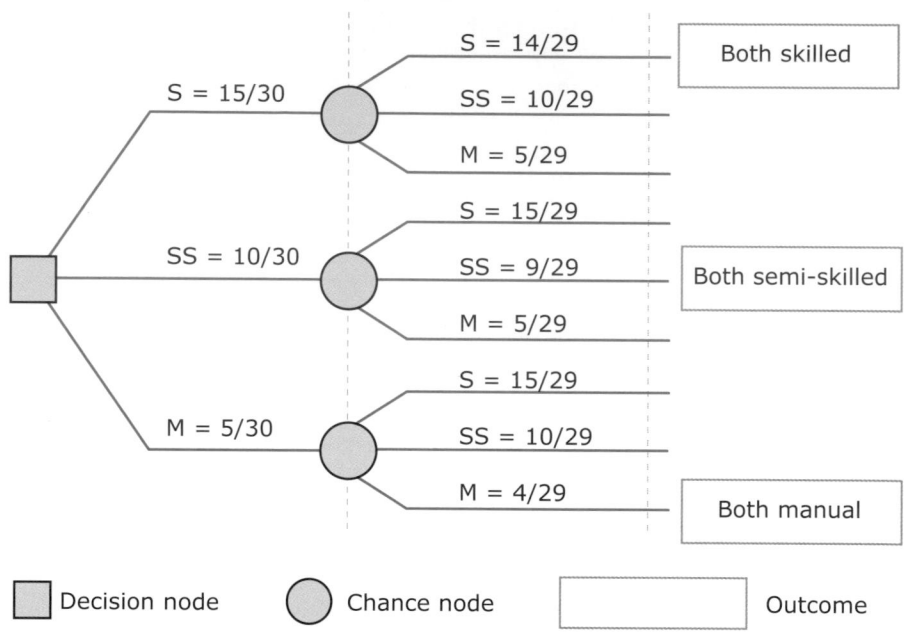

Figure 51   Decision tree

The probability of both workers being of the same grade can be calculated using the above decision tree. Each main branch ends in a chance node, from which stems three sub-branches, one of which matches the same skill as the main branch. The probability on the main branch is multiplied by the probability of the same skill on one of the three sub-branches.

$$P(\text{both skilled}) = \frac{15}{30} \times \frac{14}{29} = \frac{7}{29}$$

$$P(\text{both semi-skilled}) = \frac{10}{30} \times \frac{9}{29} = \frac{3}{29}$$

$$P(\text{both manual}) = \frac{5}{30} \times \frac{4}{29} = \frac{2}{87}$$

The probability of the two representatives being of the same grade is therefore:

$$\frac{7}{29} + \frac{3}{29} + \frac{2}{87} = \frac{32}{87} \text{ (i.e., about 37\%).}$$

4.2 Expected values

The probability theory covered above can be used to provide useful information to management by quantifying various options. Where options have values (such as cost and revenue or profit) as well as probabilities attached to them, the concept of expected values can be used. The **expected value** of a particular action is the sum of the values of each possible outcome multiplied by its probability.

An expected value can be defined as the weighted average value based on probabilities:

expected value (EV) = $\sum xp$ (i.e., the sum of each outcome times the probability)

where

$\sum$ = sum of

x = outcome

p = probability of the outcome occurring

The following example uses probability theory to calculate the expected value of the daily takings of a coffee shop at an airport, where the coffee is sold at £2.50 per cup.

By summarising the record of sales over several weeks into a frequency distribution, it can be seen that sales vary, very conveniently, in multiples of 50 cups:

Number of cups of coffee sold	Percentage of days
100	20
150	25
200	30
250	20
300	5

Assuming the pattern above continues, the expected value of sales over 100 days can be calculated by multiplying the number of cups sold by the selling price of £2.50, multiplying by the probability and summing the total.

Takings (£) (x)	Frequency (f)	fx
250	20	5,000
375	25	9,375
500	30	15,000
625	20	12,500
750	5	3,750
	100	45,625

The expected value of sales per day will be £45,625/100 = £456.25. The vendor would not expect his daily takings to be £456.25: they would be £250, £375, £500, £625 or £750. However, £456.25 is what the expected average daily takings would be in the long run.

Probability theory can also be used to assist managers in decision making. If two or more courses of action are open to a business, past experience can be used to calculate the expected values from each action. For example, if a number of projects is under consideration, the expected value of each can be compared with one another. If a project has a positive expected value, the project can be accepted. If a project has a negative expected value, it should be rejected. Where all courses of action show a positive expected value, the action with the highest expected value should be undertaken.

For example, assume that a company is opening a new department store and three possible sites are available. Market research suggests that the success of each site and its likely annual profits will be:

Site	Probability of success	Profit	Probability of failure	Profit/(loss)
A	0.8	£630,000	0.2	(£200,000)
B	0.7	£650,000	0.3	£100,000
C	0.6	£500,000	0.4	£300,000

Where would the accountant recommend that the new department store should be situated?

The expected profits for each site need to be worked out and then compared.

Site A

P(success) = £630,000 × 0.8 = £504,000

P(failure) = (£200,000) × 0.2 = (£40,000)

Expected profits   £464,000

Site B

P(success) = £650,000 × 0.7 = £455,000

P(failure) = £100,000 × 0.3   = £30,000

Expected profits   £485,000

Site C

P(success) = £500,000 × 0.6 = £300,000

P(failure) = £300,000 × 0.4 = £120,000

Expected profits   £420,000

Based on the above calculations the new department store should be located on site B, as it gives the highest expected profits. The average profits are expected to be £485,000 per annum over a number of years.

Looking at this example, it can be seen that expected values, like all averages, have strengths and limitations.

Strengths

- Easy to understand and to calculate.
- The whole distribution is represented.
- Takes account arithmetically of the expected values of all possible outcomes.

Limitations

- As the whole distribution is represented by one figure, it ignores other facets of the distribution, such as the range.
- Assumes that the decision maker is risk neutral, that is, it takes no account of risk. For example, the following two alternative projects would be ranked equally, as they both have the same expected value. However, personal attitudes to risk vary.

Project 1

	£	p	
Optimistic outcome	55,000	0.2	
Most likely outcome	25,000	0.6	
Pessimistic outcome	5,000	0.2	EV = £27,000

Project 2

	£	p	
Optimistic outcome	30,000	0.25	
Most likely outcome	27,000	0.50	
Pessimistic outcome	24,000	0.25	EV = £27,000

Project 1 has a wide range of outcomes. At best it would produce £55,000, at worst only £5,000. With Project 2 there is only £6,000 difference between the best and worst outcomes.

Strictly speaking, expected values should only be used where data are obtained from a large number of observations as in a frequency distribution.

4.3 Normal distribution

Where a large number of observations has been made and a frequency distribution drawn up, that frequency distribution can be shown diagrammatically in a histogram (see Section 2.5).

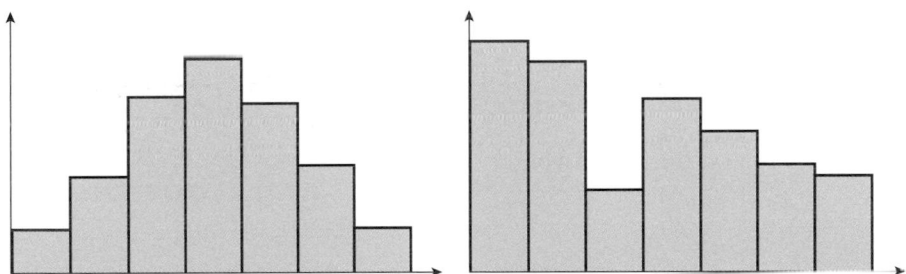

Figure 52   Two histograms

The histogram on the left in Figure 52 is symmetrical. If it were converted to a line graph (by joining the mid-points of each data class), the graph would appear as an inverted V shape, as in Figure 53.

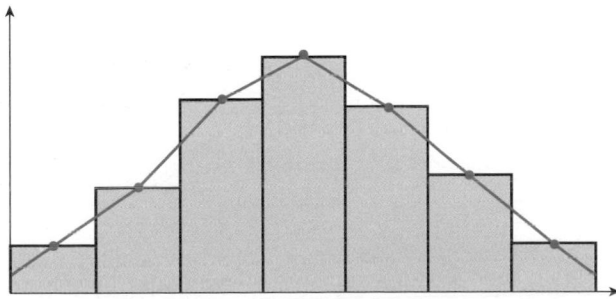

Figure 53   Normal distribution line graph superimposed on a histogram

If the number of data classes is increased, the graph will become approximately bell-shaped. This is known as a **normal distribution curve**. There are other distributions, but they are not covered in this module.

For a set of data to have a normal distribution, it needs to satisfy three criteria, as follows.

1   The items must be drawn from a *continuous* distribution. For example, the number of children someone has would not be suitable, because you can have only *discrete* numbers of children: 0, 1, 2, etc. An example of a continuous distribution is where something can be measured, for example, waiting times.

2   The items must be independent, that is, the first reading must not influence the second reading.

3   The variables being measured must have an expected value for the mean, but, since they are subject to sources of random differences, each is as likely to be in a positive direction as in a negative direction from the mean.

4.3.1   Features and properties of a normal distribution curve

A normal distribution (or normal curve) has the following features:

•   It is bell-shaped and symmetrical, so the area under the curve to the right of the mean is equal to the area to the left of the mean. While it may be tall and thin or low and spread out, it will always have the characteristic, symmetrical bell shape.

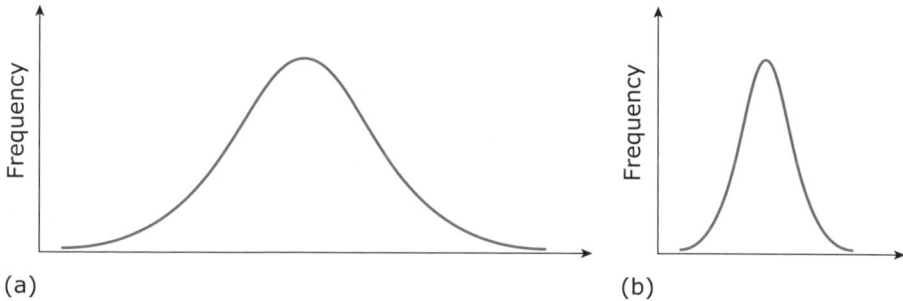

Figure 54   Normal distribution curves: (a) a wide distribution; and (b) a narrow distribution

- The mean, mode and median are at the same point on the x axis and lie at the peak of the curve. Note that the mean of the population is represented by the symbol μ (pronounced 'mew' to rhyme with 'few').

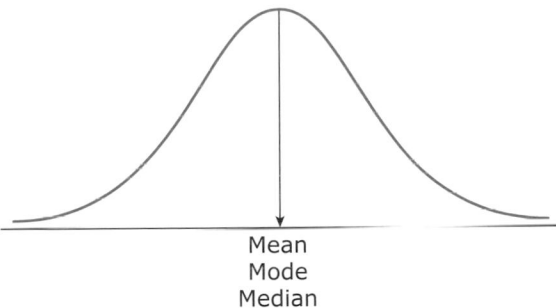

Figure 55   Normal distribution curve showing mean, mode and median

- Both tails of the distribution approach, but never reach, the x axis

One of the most useful properties of the normal distribution is that the likelihood of any reading from the continuous distribution is known to be within a set number of standard deviations of the mean. For any normal distribution the following figures hold true.

68.26% of readings occur within ± one standard deviation (σ)

95.45% of readings occur within ± two standard deviations (2σ)

99.74% of readings occur within ± three standard deviations (3σ)

It is common to round these percentages to 68%, 95% and 99.7%. Remember that the total area under the normal distribution curve is 100%.

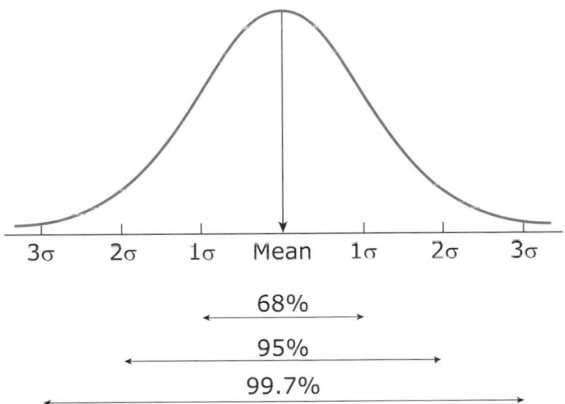

Figure 56   Properties of a normal distribution

4.3.2   Use of normal distribution tables

The area under a normal distribution curve can be found by using the 1-tailed normal distribution tables. These can be found at the end of Session 4. The tables are called 1-tailed and show the proportion under the entire curve which is between $z = 0$ and a positive value of z. Areas for negative values of z can be obtained from the same table by symmetry. The **Z value** is the distance above or below the mean. It is expressed as a number of standard deviations.

It has already been said that 68.26% of readings occur within ± one standard deviation from the mean. If you look down the left-hand column of the normal distribution table for $z = 1.0$ standard deviation (σ) and read across the table to 0.00, the figure shown is 0.3413. This is the reading for one standard deviation either to the left or to the right of the mean (μ). To obtain the figure for ± one standard deviation, you need to multiply this figure by 2, which gives 0.6826 or 68.26%. (Remember that there is one standard deviation to the left of the mean and one to the right of the mean.)

Let us look at some examples.

Find the area under the normal curve between $z = 0$ and $z = 1.4$

Using the table on page 108 look down the column marked z until you reach 1.4. Then look across to the column marked 0.00. The result is 0.4192, which tells you that 41.92% of the area under the normal distribution curve is between the mean and 1.4 standard deviations from the mean.

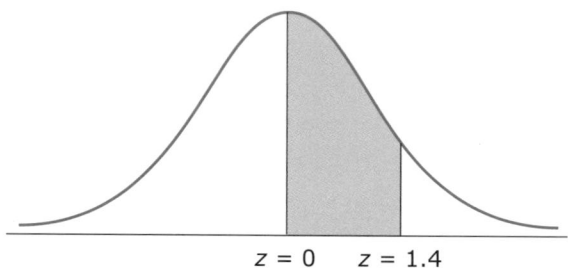

Figure 57   Area between $z = 0$ and $z = 1.4$

Find the area under the normal curve between $z = -0.86$ and $z = 0$

The area required is between $z = -0.86$ and $z = 0$. This is the same as the area between $z = 0$ and $z = 0.86$ (as both sides of the normal curve are the same). Look down the column marked z until 0.8 is reached. Then look across to the column marked 0.06. The result is 0.3051, so 30.51% of the area under the normal distribution curve lies between −0.86 standard deviations and the mean.

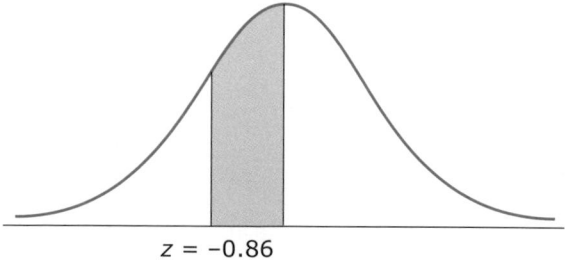

Figure 58   Area between $z = -0.86$ and $z = 0$

Find the area under the normal curve between $z = -0.28$ and $z = 2.13$

The area required is the area between $z = -0.28$ and $z = 0$ *plus* the area between $z = 0$ and $z = 2.13$.

This is 0.1103 + 0.4834 = 0.5937 or 59.37%.

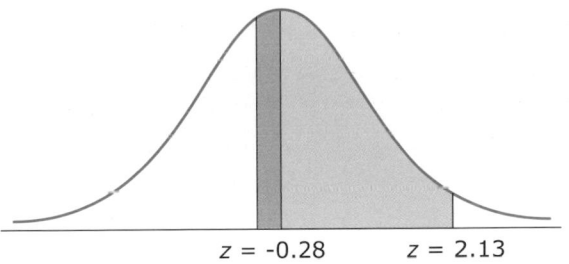

Figure 59   Area between $z = -0.28$ and $z = 2.13$

Find the area under the normal curve between $z = 0.56$ and $z = 1.88$

The area required is the area between $z = 0$ and $z = 1.88$ *minus* the area between $z = 0$ and $z = 0.56$.

This is $0.4699 - 0.2123 = 0.2576$ or 25.76%.

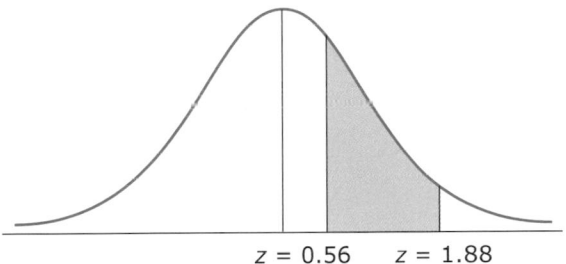

Figure 60   Area between $z = 0.56$ and $z = 1.88$

Find the area under the normal curve to the right of $z = -1.64$

The area required is the area between $z - -1.64$ and $z = 0$ *plus* the area to the right of $z = 0$.

This is $0.4495 + 0.5 = 0.9495$ or 94.95%.

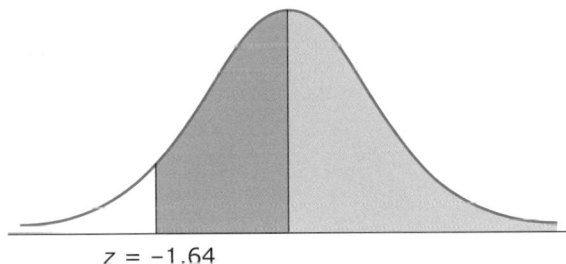

Figure 61   Area to the right of $z = -1.64$

Activity 4.5 ....

Calculate the area under a normal curve between $z = -0.72$ and $z = -1.93$.

Feedback ....

Looking at the normal distribution table, $z = -1.93$ corresponds to an area of 0.4732, and $z = -0.72$ to 0.2642; 0.4732 minus 0.2642 is 0.2090 or 20.9%. You will probably find it helpful to draw a rough diagram.

As the normal distribution curve is symmetrical, you can find the proportion of any area under the curve if you know the mean and standard deviation of a normal distribution.

Figure 62 shows the standard deviations of a normal distribution curve.

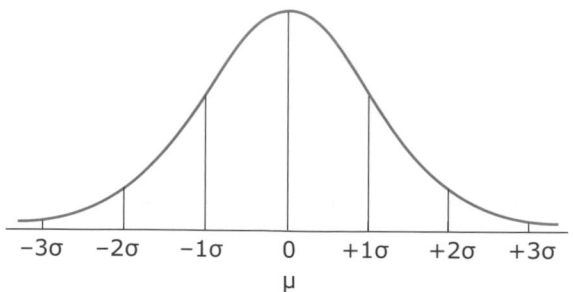

Figure 62   Standard deviations of a normal distribution curve

The area under the curve that lies in the range 80 to 85 can be found, if the frequency distribution is known to have a mean of 100 and a standard deviation of 10.

1   Calculate the area between 80 and the mean.

   The area under the curve between 80 and 100 is 2 standard deviations from the mean. Looking at the normal distribution table, you can see that this area is 0.4772.

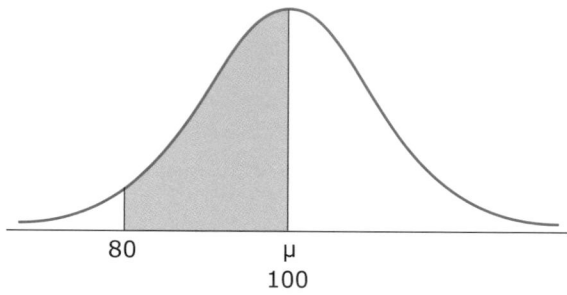

Figure 63   Area between 80 and the mean

2   Calculate the area between 85 and the mean.

   The area under the curve between 85 and 100 is 1.5 standard deviations from the mean. Looking at the normal distribution table, it is clear that this area is 0.4332.

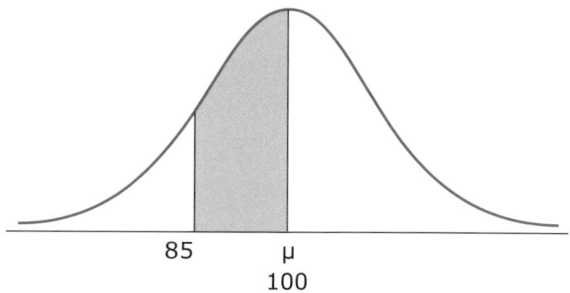

Figure 64   Area under the curve between 85 and 100

3   Deduct the answer to part 2 from the answer to part 1.

Area between 80 and the mean   0.4772

Area between 85 and the mean   0.4332

Area between 80 and 85   0.0440

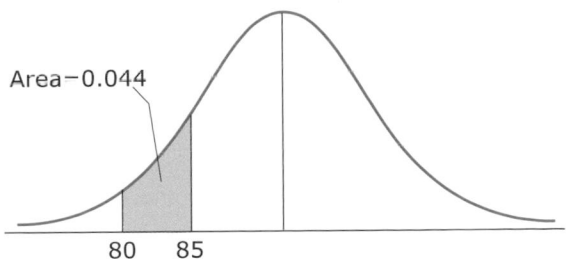

Figure 65   Area between 80 and 85 = 0.044

Activity 4.6 ....

A frequency distribution has a mean of 150 and a standard deviation of 20. Find the area under the normal curve that lies in the range 112 and 140.

Feedback ....

We can find the area under the curve that lies in the range 112 to 140, as we know that the frequency distribution has a mean of 150 and a standard deviation of 20.

1   Calculate the area between 112 and the mean.

The area under the curve between 112 and 150 is 1.9 standard deviations from the mean. Looking at the normal distribution tables we see that this area is 0.4713.

2   Calculate the area between 140 and the mean.

The area under the curve between 140 and 150 is 0.5 standard deviations from the mean. Looking at the normal distribution tables we see that this area is 0.1915.

3   Deduct the answer to part 2 from the answer to part 1.

Area between 112 and the mean	0.4713
Area between 140 and the mean	0.1915
Area between 112 and 140	0.2798

4.3.3   Business applications of the normal distribution curve

The normal distribution and its properties can be used to help managers with a range of business problems.

- Dimensions of manufactured goods, for example, to determine the percentage of defective washers produced by a machine.

- Quality control, for example, problems involving the filling of tins, jars and bottles by automated machines.

- Child development, for example, to work out how many pupils in a junior school are over a certain recommended healthy weight.

- Service or waiting times, for example, in a fast-food restaurant to work out how many employees are needed to ensure that customers are served within a reasonable time period.

- Time taken for journeys, for example, in a transport company to establish the average journey time to use as a comparator.

Let us look at a business example.

A company fills and sells 250g bags of flour. The weight of flour delivered to a bag by the filling machine is normally distributed about the required weight with a standard deviation of 2g. For quality control purposes bags should not weigh less than 246g. What is the probability that a bag weighs less than 246g?

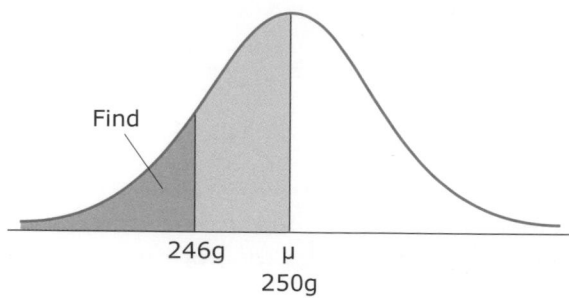

Figure 66   Normal distribution: the probability that a bag weighs less than 246g

To calculate the proportion of bags containing less than 246g, the area between the 246 and the mean of 250 needs to be found and then deducted from the area under half of the curve.

$$z = \frac{x - \mu}{\sigma} = \frac{246 - 250}{2} = \frac{-4}{2} = -2.00$$

The minus sign can be ignored, as it merely indicates that −4 is 2.00 standard deviations below the mean, while the normal distribution is symmetrical.

Reading from the normal distribution tables (first down the z column, then across), z is 0.4772 and, as the only interest is in the probability that a bag weighs less than 246g (the dark shaded area in Figure 66), 0.4772 needs to be deducted from 0.5.

0.5 − 0.4772 = 0.0228, so 2.28% of bags weigh less than 246g, which is a low percentage and would not cause problems with weights and measures regulations. If the result were 12.5%, this would be quite high and might cause problems.

Activity 4.7   ....

Simpson Ltd sells fruit and vegetables to the wholesale market. Its salesmen's salaries are normally distributed with a mean of £20,000 and a standard deviation of £3,500.

Calculate:

(a) The proportion of salesmen who earn less than £17,000.

(b) The proportion of salesmen who earn between £12,000 and £17,000.

Feedback   ....

(a) The proportion of salesmen who earn less than £17,000:

x = 17,000, μ = 20,000, σ = 3,500

$$z = \frac{x - \mu}{\sigma} = \frac{17,000 - 20,000}{3,500} = -0.86$$

Looking at the normal distribution table, z = 0.86 corresponds to an area of 0.3051. As half the area under the normal distribution curve is 0.5, the required area is 0.5 − 0.3051, which is 0.1949 or 19.49%. So 19.49% of salesmen earn less than £17,000.

(b) The proportion of salesmen who earn between £12,000 and £17,000.
First, find the proportion of salesmen who earn less than £12,000:

$x = 12,000$, $\mu = 20,000$, $\sigma = 3,500$

$$z = \frac{x - \mu}{\sigma} = \frac{12,000 - 20,000}{3,500} = -2.29$$

Looking at the normal distribution table, $z = 2.29$ corresponds to 0.4890, so the required area is 0.5 – 0.489, which is 0.011 or 1.1%.

Therefore the proportion of salesmen who earn between £12,000 and £17,000 is 19.49% (as calculated above) less 1.1% = 18.39%.

4.4 Decision making under uncertainty

When it is known that things can turn out in different ways but it is impossible to assign probabilities to each outcome, this is known as decision making under uncertainty.

Most business decisions are decisions involving uncertainty, the features of which are as follows.

- There is a choice of several possible courses of action.

- Each possible course may have several outcomes which depend on factors that are uncertain.

- The choice of possible course will depend on the criteria used in making that choice. For instance, the decision maker may be risk averse (avoids risk, the pessimistic view), or a risk seeker (happy taking risks, the optimist).

This section looks at three quantitative approaches to decision making under uncertainty:

- the Maximax decision rule
- the Maximin decision rule
- the Minimax 'Regret' decision rule.

Maximax decision rule: the optimistic view

The optimist assumes that the best outcome will occur and so chooses the course with the best possible pay-off (maximise the maximum possible pay-off).

Maximin decision rule: the pessimistic view

The pessimist's view assumes that the worst outcome will occur and so chooses the course with the least bad/worst pay-off (maximise the minimum pay-off).

Minimax 'Regret' decision rule: an alternative approach based on the pessimistic view

Not wishing to make the wrong decision, the strategy here will be to minimise the maximum regret or opportunity loss through making the wrong decision.

How these approaches work

These three approaches will be looked at using the following data.

Mr Friel has decided to expand his business and is considering introducing one of three possible new products: X, Y and Z. The following table shows the likely contribution (gains) in £'000 for each product under the possible market conditions. It is assumed that each market condition is equally likely. Which product should Mr Friel produce, based on each of the three strategies: Maximax, Maximin and Minimax Regret?

Market conditions	Product demand		
	X	Y	Z
Favourable	13	20	27
Average	2	10	1
Poor	−16	3	−45

Using the Maximax strategy

This is based on the optimist's decision rule. The optimist assumes that the best possible outcome will occur and so chooses the course with the best possible pay-off.

The best pay-off for each product will be identified, then, the product with the greatest potential will be chosen, that is, Product Z.

	X	Y	Z
Best pay-off	13	20	27
			▲

Using the Maximin strategy

This is based on the pessimistic/cautious (risk-averse) approach. The pessimist assumes that the worst possible outcome will occur so chooses the course with the least bad/worst outcome.

The worst result for each product will be identified, then the alternative with the least bad/worst outcome will be chosen, that is, Product Y.

	X	Y	Z
Minimum	−16	3	−45
		▲	

Using the Minimax Regret strategy

This approach is based on the idea that, if the wrong decision is made, there will be an opportunity loss, that is, there will be a smaller contribution than if the correct decision had been made. This lost contribution can be considered as the value of the 'regret' at having made the wrong decision.

Step 1   For each possible outcome, determine the best choice and assign an opportunity loss or 'regret' value of zero result to this option. Hence, if the best decision choice is made, there will be zero regret. The following table shows the options with zero regret for each outcome.

Market conditions	Product demand		
	X	Y	Z
Favourable	13	20	0
Average	2	0	1
Poor	−16	0	−45

Step 2 Calculate the opportunity loss or 'regret' for each option by comparing its pay-off with the best pay-off for each outcome. This gives the following figures:

Market conditions	Best Result		Opportunity loss		
	Product	Result	X	Y	Z
Favourable	Z	27	14 (27 − 13)	7 (27 − 20)	0
Average	Y	10	8 (10 − 2)	0	9 (10 − 1)
Poor	Y	3	19 (3 − (−16))	0	48 (3 − (−45))

Step 3 The pessimist assumes the worst case scenario. The following table shows the 'regret' value for each option for each outcome. The maximum possible regret for X is 19, for Y it is 7 and for Z it is 48. Wishing to minimise the maximum regret, the pessimist will choose Y.

Market conditions	Best result		Decision		
	Product	Result	X	Y	Z
Favourable	Z	27	14	7	0
Average	Y	10	8	0	9
Poor	Y	3	19	0	48
Maximum regrets			**19**	**7**	**48**
				▲	

In discussing decision making under uncertainty, not all the possible choices of decision criteria were covered. In business, decisions are sometimes made on the basis of intuition alone, without any systematic quantifiable analysis such as that undertaken here.

Summary

In this session risk and uncertainty were defined.

Decision making under risk by assigning probabilities was discussed and the basic concept of probability was introduced. Different probabilities can be expressed on a scale of 0 to 1 representing impossible (0%, i.e., zero probability) to certain (100% probability). How probabilities of combined events can be calculated using the three laws of probability (the law of proportions, the addition law and the multiplication law) was also discussed.

Conditional probability, decision trees and expected values were looked at before discussing the nature of normal curves and how normal distribution tables can be used in probability calculations.

The session ended with a look at decision making under uncertainty by discussing its features before looking at three quantitative approaches. Maximax, Maximin and Minimax Regret were considered.

The next session introduces you to techniques used in making long-term capital investment decisions.

Normal distribution table – 1-tailed

An entry in this table is for 1-tailed tests. It shows the proportion under the entire curve which is between $z = 0$ and a positive value of z. Areas for negative values of z are obtained by symmetry.

$z = \dfrac{x - \mu}{\sigma}$ Areas of a standard normal distribution

z	0.00	0.01	0.02	0.03	0.04	0.05	0.06	0.07	0.08	0.09
0.0	0.000	0.0040	0.0080	0.0120	0.0160	0.0199	0.0239	0.0279	0.0319	0.0359
0.1	0.0398	0.0438	0.0478	0.0517	0.0557	0.0596	0.0636	0.0675	0.0714	0.0753
0.2	0.0793	0.0832	0.0871	0.0910	0.0948	0.0987	0.1026	0.1064	0.1103	0.1141
0.3	0.1179	0.1217	0.1255	0.1293	0.1331	0.1368	0.1406	0.1443	0.1480	0.1517
0.4	0.1554	0.1591	0.1628	0.1664	0.1700	0.1736	0.1772	0.1808	0.1844	0.1879
0.5	0.1915	0.1950	0.1985	0.2019	0.2054	0.2088	0.2123	0.2157	0.2190	0.2224
0.6	0.2257	0.2291	0.2324	0.2357	0.2389	0.2422	0.2454	0.2486	0.2517	0.2549
0.7	0.2580	0.2611	0.2642	0.2673	0.2703	0.2734	0.2764	0.2794	0.2823	0.2852
0.8	0.2881	0.2910	0.2939	0.2967	0.2995	0.3023	0.3051	0.3078	0.3106	0.3133
0.9	0.3159	0.3186	0.3212	0.3238	0.3264	0.3289	0.3315	0.3340	0.3365	0.3389
1.0	0.3413	0.3438	0.3461	0.3485	0.3508	0.3531	0.3553	0.3577	0.3599	0.3621
1.1	0.3643	0.3665	0.3686	0.3708	0.3729	0.3749	0.3770	0.3790	0.3810	0.3830
1.2	0.3849	0.3869	0.3888	0.3907	0.3925	0.3944	0.3962	0.3980	0.3997	0.4015
1.3	0.4032	0.4049	0.4066	0.4082	0.4099	0.4115	0.4131	0.4147	0.4162	0.4177
1.4	0.4192	0.4207	0.4222	0.4236	0.4251	0.4265	0.4279	0.4292	0.4306	0.4319
1.5	0.4332	0.4345	0.4357	0.4370	0.4382	0.4394	0.4406	0.4418	0.4429	0.4441
1.6	0.4452	0.4463	0.4474	0.4484	0.4495	0.4505	0.4515	0.4525	0.4535	0.4545
1.7	0.4554	0.4564	0.4573	0.4582	0.4591	0.4599	0.4608	0.4616	0.4625	0.4633
1.8	0.4641	0.4649	0.4656	0.4664	0.4671	0.4678	0.4686	0.4693	0.4699	0.4706
1.9	0.4713	0.4719	0.4726	0.4732	0.4738	0.4744	0.4750	0.4756	0.4761	0.4767
2.0	0.4772	0.4778	0.4783	0.4788	0.4793	0.4798	0.4803	0.4808	0.4812	0.4817
2.1	0.4821	0.4826	0.4830	0.4834	0.4838	0.4842	0.4846	0.4850	0.4854	0.4857
2.2	0.4861	0.4864	0.4868	0.4871	0.4875	0.4878	0.4881	0.4884	0.4887	0.4890
2.3	0.4891	0.4896	0.4898	0.4901	0.4904	0.4906	0.4909	0.4911	0.4913	0.4916
2.4	0.4918	0.4920	0.4922	0.4925	0.4927	0.4929	0.4931	0.4932	0.4934	0.4936
2.5	0.4938	0.4940	0.4941	0.4943	0.4945	0.4946	0.4948	0.4949	0.4951	0.4952
2.6	0.4953	0.4955	0.4956	0.4957	0.4959	0.4960	0.4961	0.4962	0.4963	0.4964
2.7	0.4965	0.4966	0.4967	0.4968	0.4969	0.4970	0.4971	0.4972	0.4973	0.4974
2.8	0.4974	0.4975	0.4976	0.4977	0.4977	0.4978	0.4979	0.4979	0.4980	0.4981
2.9	0.4981	0.4982	0.4982	0.4983	0.4984	0.4984	0.4985	0.4985	0.4986	0.4986
3.0	0.4987	0.4987	0.4987	0.4988	0.4988	0.4989	0.4989	0.4989	0.4990	0.4990

SESSION 5 Financial mathematics and investment appraisal

Introduction

Upon completion of Session 5, you are expected to be able to:

- calculate future values of an investment using both simple and compound interest
- calculate the present value of a future sum, using both a formula and discount tables
- calculate the present value of an annuity using both a formula and discount tables
- use the accounting rate of return method to evaluate a prospective capital investment
- use the payback period method to evaluate a prospective capital investment
- use the net present value method to evaluate a prospective capital investment
- use the internal rate of return method to evaluate a prospective capital investment
- understand the strengths and limitations of each of the four capital investment appraisal methods
- describe some of the non-financial factors that can influence the capital investment decision process.

This session introduces basic financial mathematical capital investment appraisal methods for management accountants.

5.1 Simple and compound interest

If you open a savings account with a bank or building society, you will need to decide whether you want to take the interest out each year or leave it in to earn interest with your original investment.

If you invest £1,000 at an interest rate of 10% for 5 years and decide to take out the interest annually, each year you will receive interest of:

£1,000 × 10% = £100

The total amount of interest you will have earned will be £1,000 × 5 years × 10% = £500. At the end of the 5 years, provided that you kept the interest, you will have £1,500. This is known as simple interest and can be calculated using the formula:

$$I = P \times r \times n$$

where

I = the total interest earned

P = the principal, the sum invested

r = the rate of interest expressed as an annual interest rate

n = number of interest bearing periods, usually expressed in years

So I = £1,000 × 0.10 × 5 = £500.

Simple interest is interest earned/paid based only on the principal sum invested. The interest is not reinvested to earn more interest.

Compound interest is interest earned/paid on the principal sum invested plus the reinvested interest. If you had decided to leave your annual interest in the bank or building society account so that the interest earned also earns interest, then the interest you receive after five years would be:

	£	Interest £
Amount invested	1,000	
Interest in year 1	100	100
Amount at end of year 1	1,100	
Interest in year 2	110	110
Amount at end of year 2	1,210	
Interest in year 3	121	121
Amount at end of year 3	1,331	
Interest in year 4	133	133
Amount at end of year 4	1,464	
Interest in year 5	146	146
Investment value at the end of year 5	1,610	
Interest earned		*610

* Ignoring pence

The compound interest formula is:

$$S = P(1 + r)^n$$

where

S = a sum arising in the future

P = the sum at the present time

r = annual interest rate

n = number of interest bearing periods, usually expressed in years

$$S = £1,000(1 + 0.10)^5 = £1,610.51$$

The interest rate given for various forms of consumer credit is quoted as a monthly rate. A credit card agreement, for instance, may say that interest is charged at 2.25% per month. However, to be able to compare the rate with other forms of interest it is useful to know the **annual percentage rate (APR)**, that is, the actual annual rate of interest.

For example, suppose that there was a balance on the credit card of £100 on 1 January 20X1 and the holder of the card decided not to pay it until 1 January 20X2. At the end of the first month the interest charged would be £100 × 2.25% = £2.25 and this would be added to the balance on the credit card at 31 January 20X1. At the end of the next month, more interest would be added this time – £102.25 × 2.25% = £2.30 so the balance due at the end of February 20X1 would be £102.25 + £2.30 = £104.55 to two decimal places. So you can see that the interest is compounding.

This is known as a geometric progression and rather than writing it out in full, the formula above, $S = P(1+r)^n$, can be adapted to $V = X(1+r)^n$ to find the amount at the end of the period (V). X = the original sum and, as before, r = the interest rate and n = number of interest bearing periods.

$$V = X(1+r)^n, \text{ so } £100(1+0.0225)^{12} = £130.60$$

The APR (which is shown in the formula as r^a) can be worked out as follows:

$100 \times (1 + r^a) = £130.60$, so $100 + 100r^a = £130.60$ and thus $r^a = 0.3060$, so the value of the APR is 30.6%.

What appears to be a low interest rate of 2.25% a month is actually quite a high annual rate of 30.6%.

5.2 The present value of a future sum of money

When looking at simple and compound interest, you saw how much a sum invested today would be worth at a future point in time. However, what if you knew you needed £1,000 in 3 years' time, how much would you have to save if you could invest money at 5% at your building society? The question actually being asked is: what is the **present value** of £1,000 receivable in 3 years' time, if the compound interest rate is 5%?

The present value (PV) of a future sum can be calculated using the formula:

$$PV = \frac{S}{(1+r)^n}$$

where

S = a sum arising in the future

r = the rate of interest

n = the number of years

This formula is merely a manipulation of the compound interest formula used at the end of Section 5.1, with PV replacing P.

So $\dfrac{£1,000}{(1+0.05)^3}$ = £864, rounded to the nearest pound

This means that investing £864 today at 5% compound interest for 3 years would give the required £1,000 in 3 years' time.

This is a very easy calculation using a scientific calculator. Just enter

⌨ 1,000 ⊙ (1 + .05) $\boxed{x^\blacksquare}$ 3 =

Present value tables can be used in place of a calculator. They are on pages 135 and 136. Note there are two tables, Table 1 and Table 2.

Using Table 1 'Present value of £1 at compound interest' to work out the present value in the formula above, you would look across the figures at the top until you found 5, corresponding to the 5% interest rate. Next, you would look down the column for the figure shown opposite the year 3 and then multiply this figure of 0.8638 by the £1,000 to arrive at £863.8 which rounds up to £864.

Finding a present value from a future value is known as **discounting**. In the example above, you discounted (or found the present value of) one future sum. However, what if there were a series of future cash flows that were to be discounted to obtain a present value?

For example, what is the present value of receiving £3,000 in one year's time, £5,000 in 2 years' time, £7,000 in 3 years' time and £9,000 in four years' time? The interest rate is 10%.

Using a calculator the answer would be:

$$\frac{3,000}{(1+0.10)^1} + \frac{5,000}{(1+0.10)^2} + \frac{7,000}{(1+0.10)^3} + \frac{9,000}{(1+0.10)^4}$$
$$= 2,727 + 4,132 + 5,259 + 6,147 = £18,265$$

Scientific calculator

When entering $\dfrac{5000}{(1+0.10)^2}$ enter 🖮 5000 ▼ (1 + 0.10) $\boxed{x^2}$

Using the discount tables, the discount factors will be 0.9091, 0.8264, 0.7513 and 0.6830, so the calculation becomes:

$$PV = 3,000 \times 0.9091 + 5,000 \times 0.8264 + 7,000 \times 0.7513$$
$$+ 9,000 \times 0.6830$$
$$= £18,265$$

5.3 Present value of an annuity

An **annuity** is the promise of a fixed sum per annum for a number of years.

To find the present value of an annuity, multiply the annual sum received by $\dfrac{1-(1+r)^{-n}}{r}$, where r = the discount rate and n = the number of years.

Rather than calculating this figure, an annuity table can be used. One is given on page 136: Table 2 'Present value of an annuity of 1'.

To find the value of £1,200 p.a. received every year for 6 years at 8% per annum, you look across the table to find 8% interest rate; then go down the column until you reach 6 years. This gives 4.6229. Multiply this by £1,200, which gives £5,547 (to the nearest pound). Remember to push the $\boxed{\text{S·D}}$ key on your scientific calculator if the answer is shown as a fraction.

5.4 An introduction to capital investment appraisal

In order for an organisation to grow or adapt to changes in a dynamic economic and marketing environment, managers must undertake capital investment programmes. Such investment decisions are for the long run, involving making a capital outlay, usually cash, at one point in time with the expectation of receiving future economic benefit (returns). Capital investment decisions include purchasing a new building, purchasing a new piece of equipment, and extending an existing factory building.

Businesses worldwide generally use one or more of the following four techniques to evaluate prospective capital investments:

- accounting rate of return (ARR)
- payback
- net present value (NPV)
- internal rate of return (IRR).

The first is based on profits, while the other three are based on cash flows and are therefore to be preferred for the following reasons.

- Cash inflows are objective and tangible, while profits are worked out using accounting conventions and are thus more subjective and intangible.
- Items such as capital and revenue expenditure, inventory valuation and depreciation calculations can be manipulated to produce a range of possible options in measuring profits.
- The timing of cash flows is easier to plan, as they are factual.

NPV and IRR methods discount the future cash flows to arrive at the present value and therefore the discussion in Section 5.2 is relevant.

There are two types of investment decision:

- a single project where a single accept or reject decision is called for
- a choice of projects where the company will select the best option (mutually exclusive projects).

In evaluating these projects it is assumed that costs and revenues arise at the end of the year to which they relate. There is one exception to this rule. The initial investment (say, in machinery) is treated as invested at the start of period 1 and this is referred to as time 0. Time 0 represents the start of period 1 and so any initial investment is shown as a present value and not discounted.

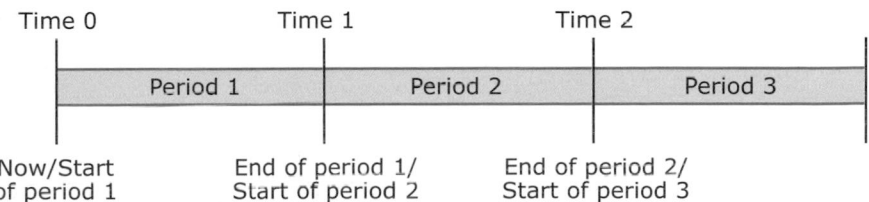

Figure 67 The cash flow timing convention

5.5 Accounting rate of return (ARR)

The **accounting rate of return (ARR),** otherwise known as the return on investment (ROI) or return on capital employed (ROCE), can be calculated using a number of different definitions.

The definition used in this module is:

$$\text{ARR} = \frac{\text{estimated average profits}}{\text{average capital employed}} \times 100$$

Other definitions include:

$$\text{ARR} = \frac{\text{estimated average profits}}{\text{initial outlay}} \times 100$$

and

$$\text{ARR} = \frac{\text{estimated total profit}}{\text{initial outlay}} \times 100$$

The definition that is chosen should be used consistently.

As the accounting rate of return is based on accounting profits, it is affected by the subjectivity inherent in the measurement of accounting estimates.

Decision rule   The ARR, once calculated, is compared with the company's target rate of return.

- For a single project – use a simple accept or reject decision; if the ARR from the project exceeds the company's target rate of return, the project should be undertaken.

- For two or more projects which are mutually exclusive, the ARR should be compared for all projects and the project with the highest ARR (provided that it exceeds the company's target rate of return) should be undertaken.

5.5.1   ARR and a single project

Spindlewood Limited is considering investing in a new wood-turning machine:

Cost of the new machine	£100,000
Estimated useful life	5 years
Residual (disposal) value	nil
Depreciation (straight-line method)	20%
Estimated profits before depreciation	
Year 1	£21,000
Year 2	£25,000
Year 3	£36,000
Year 4	£38,000
Year 5	£20,000

The company's target accounting rate of return is 15%.

Calculation of the ARR

	£
Total profits before depreciation	140,000
Total profits after depreciation	40,000
Average annual profit after depreciation	8,000
Cost of new machine	100,000
Average net book value* over 5 years (as there is no disposal value)	50,000

* Also known as the average investment $= \dfrac{\text{cost of machine} + \text{disposal value}}{2}$

$= \dfrac{£100,000 + 0}{2} = £50,000$.

$$\text{ARR} = \frac{\text{estimated average profits}}{\text{average capital employed}} \times 100 = \frac{8,000}{50,000} \times 100 = 16\%$$

As this exceeds the company's target accounting rate of return of 15%, the project should be accepted.

5.5.2 ARR and mutually exclusive projects

Glenwood Parts needs to buy a new machine. Two models are available, A and B, but one has a higher production capacity than the other.

	Machine	
	A	B
Cost of the new machine	£100,000	£120,000
Estimated useful life	5 years	5 years
Residual (disposal) value	nil	£30,000
Depreciation (straight-line method)	20%	20%
Estimated profits before depreciation		
Year 1	£21,500	£26,000
Year 2	£32,000	£32,000
Year 3	£37,000	£35,000
Year 4	£44,000	£39,000
Year 5	£18,000	£29,250

The company's target accounting rate of return is 15%.

Calculation of the ARR

	Machine A	Machine B
	£	£
Total profits before depreciation	152,500	161,250
Total profits after depreciation	52,500	71,250
Average annual profit after depreciation	10,500	14,250
Cost of new machine	100,000	120,000
Average net book value* over 5 years	50,000	75,000

* The average net book value over 5 years is calculated as follows:

$$\text{average investment} = \frac{\text{cost of machine} + \text{disposal value}}{2}$$

$$\text{Machine A} = \frac{£100,000 + £0}{2} = £50,000$$

$$\text{Machine B} = \frac{£120,000 + £30,000}{2} = £75,000$$

The accounting rate of return is:

$$\text{ARR} = \frac{\text{estimated average profits}}{\text{average capital employed}} \times 100$$

	Machine A	Machine B
ARR	$\dfrac{£10,500}{£50,000} \times 100 = 21\%$	$\dfrac{£14,250}{£75,000} \times 100 = 19\%$

Both projects have an ARR in excess of the company's target accounting rate of return of 15%, so as only one of the machines is needed, the management accountant would advise that machine A should be chosen, as this has the higher ARR.

Activity 5.1

Consider an investment of £10,000 in an asset that produces cash flows for the next four years of £2,000, £3,000, £4,000 and £5,000. The investment will have a zero scrap value at the end of the four years. For simplicity, it will be assumed that the only accounting adjustment to be made is depreciation (but in a real life situation there would be other adjustments, such as bad debt (irrecoverable receivable) provisions and accruals). Assume that straight-line depreciation is used.

(a) Calculate the accounting profit for each year.

(b) Calculate the average capital employed.

(c) Calculate the average ARR (for the 4 year period).

(d) Calculate the ARR for each year, based on estimated annual profits and average capital employed.

Feedback

(a) Depreciating an asset worth £10,000 over four years using the straight-line depreciation method gives a depreciation figure of £2,500 per annum. The annual accounting profits would therefore appear as follows:

	Year 1	Year 2	Year 3	Year 4
	£	£	£	£
Cash flows	2,000	3,000	4,000	5,000
Annual depreciation	(2,500)	(2,500)	(2,500)	(2,500)
Accounting profit/(loss)	(500)	500	1,500	2,500

(b) On a year by year basis the average capital employed will be:

$$\frac{\text{value at start of year} + \text{value at end of year}}{2}$$

The average capital employed each year is calculated by adding the opening net book value (the value of a business as shown in the balance sheet) to the net book value at the end of the year. Hence, in year 3, it is (£5,000 + £2,500)/2 = £3,750. The other values are shown in the table in part (d).

Asset value	£
	10,000
Year 1 depreciation	(2,500)
	7,500
Year 2 depreciation	(2,500)
	5,000
Year 3 depreciation	(2,500)
	2,500
Year 4 depreciation	(2,500)
	NIL

(c) The value of the asset is £10,000 at the start of year 1 and nil at the end of year 4, an average of £5,000.

So average ARR for the 4 year period $= \dfrac{£1,000^*}{£5,000} = 0.2 = 20\%$.

* The sum of the accounting profits is £4,000. Divided by 4 gives average annual profits of £1,000.

(d) The accounting rate of return is as follows:

	Year 1	Year 2	Year 3	Year 4
	£	£	£	£
Cash flows	2,000	3,000	4,000	5,000
Annual depreciation	2,500	2,500	2,500	2,500
Accounting profit	(500)	500	1,500	2,500
Average capital employed	8,750	6,250	3,750	1,250
ARR (%)	**(5.71)**	**8.0**	**40.0**	**200.0**

5.5.3 Strengths and weaknesses of the ARR

ARR has the following strengths and weaknesses:

Strengths

- It is simple to calculate.
- It gives a percentage measure (some people find this easier to understand than a specific sum).

Weaknesses

- It is a crude average method that does not take into account the timings of cash flows (future benefits).
- It is based on profits not cash flows. Profit calculations involve the use of judgements in deciding which expenditure should be classified as capital and which as revenue expenditure, the calculation of depreciation and the valuation of inventory, etc.

5.6 Payback period method

Payback looks at how quickly a project generates cash flows to pay back the initial capital expenditure. Businesses tend to use it as an additional discriminator rather than as the sole guide in the capital investment decision making process.

Consider the following example.

Glen Limited wishes to purchase a new bottling machine costing £95,000 which will generate increased cash inflows of:

Year 1	£19,000
Year 2	£28,000
Year 3	£34,000
Year 4	£36,000

To calculate the payback period, calculate the cumulative cash flow at the end of each year, until it equals the amount of the original investment, as follows.

Year	0	1	2	3	4
Cash flow (£)	(95,000)	19,000	28,000	34,000	36,000
Cumulative cash flow (£)	(95,000)	(76,000)	(48,000)	(14,000)	22,000

You can see that the initial investment will be paid back somewhere between the end of year 3 and the end of year 4. This can be expressed as 3 years 4.67 months which can be rounded up to 3 years 5 months.

$$3 \text{ years} + \left(\frac{\text{negative balance outstanding at beginning}}{\text{cash inflow in payback year}} \times 12 \right)$$

$$= 3 \text{ years} + \left(\frac{£14,000}{£36,000} \times 12 \right) = 3 \text{ years 5 months}$$

This, however, inherently assumes that cash flows arise evenly throughout a year.

Decision rule   When evaluating two or more projects, accept the project with the shortest payback period.

Activity 5.2 ....

The cash flows relating to three project proposals are:

	Project net cash flows (£)		
Year	A	B	C
0	(6,000)	(6,000)	(6,000)
1	3,000	3,000	3,000
2	2,000	2,000	3,000
3	2,000	1,000	–
4	2,000	1,000	–
5	1,000	–	–
6	1,000	–	–

Calculate the payback for each of these projects. Which project do you consider preferable and what does that tell you about the limitations of payback period?

Feedback ....

Payback period for project A is 2.5 years; project B is 3 years; project C is 2 years.

Project C gives the shortest payback period. However, both projects A and B generate greater overall cash flows. If payback were used without reference to any other capital investment appraisal technique, project C would be selected, despite it clearly being the worst of the three proposals in terms of their overall cash flows. Only when recovering the cash invested quickly was the greatest priority, would it be considered appropriate to adopt project C. Even then, it is unlikely that project C would be a suitable investment, because although the initial investment is recovered in two years, only the initial investment is recovered. There are no additional cash inflows and the cash inflows that were received in year 1 and year 2 are reduced owing to the **time value of money** (money has a different value depending upon the time at which it is received (or paid)).

This deterioration in the value of the cash flows over the two years would undoubtedly result in a loss on the project in terms of the value of money. Payback ignores these factors and hence indicates that project C should be accepted.

5.6.1   Strengths and weaknesses

The payback method has the following strengths and weaknesses:

Strengths

- It is simple to calculate and understand.
- It indicates the project which pays back the capital invested the quickest. It therefore reduces those risks facing the organisation which relate to time.
- By choosing the investment which has the quickest payback, it favours the project which enhances liquidity.

Weaknesses

- Cash flows after the payback period are ignored.
- It ignores the timing of cash flows, even within the payback period.
- Where projects have the same payback period, there is no clear decision about which project to accept and which to reject.

5.7 Net present value (NPV)

The **net present value (NPV)** method uses the concept of the **time value of money**. You will recall looking at the calculation of the present value of a future sum of money (discounting) in Section 5.2.

The NPV of a project can be defined as the value left after discounting all cash outflows and inflows attributable to a project by a chosen discount rate. The excess of discounted cash inflows over discounted cash outflows – or NPV – is simply the present economic value of the project.

Decision rule   If the calculation gives a positive result, then the project is suitable since, by definition, it will increase the net present value of the business. NPV is a function of the discount factor, the initial capital investment and estimates of future cash flows.

5.7.1   The time value of money

The first step in considering the NPV method is looking at the time value of money. Money has a time value in that £1 in the future is not the same as £1 now. This is because:

- there may be a need to sacrifice current consumption
- there may be a fall in value due to inflation
- there is a risk that the future benefit will not be received.

Consequently, providers of finance require compensation. Some projects are inherently more risky than others, so providers of finance will require a greater risk premium for riskier projects.

5.7.2   The discount rate

To convert a future cash flow to its present value, apply a **discount rate**. Some people are of the opinion that the discount rate must be based on the **cost of capital** of the firm or, to be more precise, the **weighted average cost of capital (WACC)**. The cost of capital is held to be the minimum rate of return that must be obtained by a capital investment project, and is based on the cost of servicing the capital employed by the organisation, including equity and long-term debt. In effect, it is what, on average, an organisation will need to pay in order to fund a project. One of the assumptions inherent in using the cost of capital as the discount rate is that the project appraised has the same degree of risk as the company is currently experiencing. This point will be considered in Section 5.10. The calculation of the cost of capital is a complex subject and one that is beyond the scope of this module. Should you decide to take your accountancy studies further with a view to qualifying as an accountant with chartered status, you will learn how to calculate the cost of capital.

In your B292 studies you will be told the discount rate to use.

5.7.3   Assumptions in basic discounted cash flow (DCF) appraisal

When considering basic DCF appraisal, whether it be when using the NPV method or the IRR method described in Section 5.8, a number of assumptions is made. This allows the basic principles to be discussed, and difficulties, which are beyond the scope of this module, can be ignored.

The main assumptions are:

- uncertainty does not exist
- inflation does not exist
- taxes do not exist.

5.7.4 Method of calculation

Consider the following simplified example.

A company with a weighted average cost of capital of 15% is considering purchasing a new machine. It is estimated that using the new machine costing £39,500 will increase the company's net cash inflows by the amounts shown below:

	Year 1	Year 2	Year 3
Cash inflows (£)	23,000	24,800	25,700

To find the NPV, discount the net cash flows by the discount rate that is equal to the cost of capital of the company. To find the discount factor use Table 1 of the discount tables on page 135. Table 1 provides the present value of £1 at compound interest. For example, using a 15% discount rate, multiply the year 2 cash flow by 0.7561.

	Year 0	Year 1	Year 2	Year 3
	£	£	£	£
Purchase	(39,500)			
Cash inflows		23,000	24,800	25,700
Net cash flow	(39,500)	23,000	24,800	25,700
Discount factor 15%	1.0000	0.8696	0.7561	0.6575
Present value	(39,500)	20,001	18,751	16,898
NPV (positive)	16,150			

In this case the NPV is positive so the project should be accepted. It could also be accepted if the NPV were zero, as it would neither increase nor decrease the value of the organisation. If, however, the NPV were negative, the project should be rejected, as it would decrease the value of the organisation.

The objective is to maximise the net present value of a firm's future cash flows. If several capital investment appraisals are undertaken, the NPVs can be added together to show the effect of combining investment decisions. If there is a choice between mutually exclusive proposals, then the proposal with the highest NPV should be chosen. If the capital available for investment is limited, then the proposals should be ranked by calculating each NPV relative to the investment they require, thus enabling a choice to be made of the investment(s) that produce the greatest return relative to the limited funds available.

Consider the following example.

An organisation has £20,000 available and is considering three projects, as follows.

Project	Initial investment	NPV	Relative return
A	£10,000	£2,000	20%
B	£4,000	£3,000	75%
C	£16,000	£4,000	25%

The projects can be rearranged in order of the highest relative return to choose which projects to undertake. First comes project B, followed by project C. There would be no funds remaining to undertake project A.

Project	Initial investment	NPV	Relative return	Undertake?
B	£4,000	£3,000	75%	Yes
C	£16,000	£4,000	25%	Yes
	£20,000	£7,000		◀ Combined NPV of projects
A	£10,000	£2,000	20%	No

The results of NPV calculations are very sensitive to the rate of discount chosen, and it is by no means easy to select an appropriate rate of discount.

Consider the following four projects, of which project D produces the greatest cash flow before discounting.

	Project			
Year	A	B	C	D
	£	£	£	£
0	(20,000)	(30,000)	(30,000)	(40,000)
1	0	15,000	0	5,000
2	7,500	15,000	20,000	10,000
3	0	15,000	20,000	15,000
4	15,000	12,000	20,000	25,000
5	30,000			10,000
6				10,000
7				5,000
Net cash flow	32,500	27,000	30,000	40,000

Project D has the highest net cash flow and after discounting at 10% (see below), it has the greatest NPV. If capital were freely available at 10%, this would be the preferred investment.

Discount at 10%:

	A	B	C	D
	£	£	£	£
Year 0	(20,000)	(30,000)	(30,000)	(40,000)
Years 1–7	35,071	45,499	45,215	55,575
NPV	15,071	15,499	15,215	15,575

Discount at 25%:

	A	B	C	D
	£	£	£	£
Year 0	(20,000)	(30,000)	(30,000)	(40,000)
Years 1–7	20,774	34,195	31,232	35,267
NPV	774	4,195	1,232	(4,733)

Discount at 30%:

	A	B	C	D
	£	£	£	£
Year 0	(20,000)	(30,000)	(30,000)	(40,000)
Years 1–7	17,770	31,443	27,940	30,906
NPV	(2,230)	1,443	(2,060)	(9,094)

The table has been simplified by not showing the discounting of individual amounts. This would be done using the discount tables provided at the end of this session.

If capital was rationed, at a discount rate of 10%, proposal A would have priority, since this yields the greatest NPV relative to investment (75% return on the investment of £20,000 after discounting at 10% (£15,071/£20,000 = 75%)). If a discount rate of 25% or 30% was considered appropriate, B would be the most profitable option. Thus the discount rate used and the amount of capital available have a direct impact on which project is optimal.

Activity 5.3 ....

A new machine for a factory costs £10,000 and is expected to last nine years and to produce annual savings of £6,325. It will have a scrap value of zero at the end of the nine years. What is the net present value of this project if the annual interest rate (the cost of capital and, therefore, the discount rate) is forecast to be 11%?

Use the discount tables to calculate the net present value of the project.

You have two options. Use Table 1, as in the examples above, or use Table 2.

Table 1 provides the present value of £1 at compound interest. This table should be used when the cash flows are different from year to year over the life of the project. You discount each annual cash flow by multiplying the cash flow by the discount figure in the table under the relevant year for the selected discount factor. For example, if you were using a discount rate of 10%, you would multiply the cash flow in year 5 by 0.6209.

Table 2 'Present value of an annuity of 1' can be used when the cash flows are the same over each year of the life of the project, as in this activity.

Feedback ....

The net present value can be calculated as follows. Look up the appropriate discount factor to apply (use Table 2 'Present value of an annuity of 1') in the 11% column. The project lasts nine years. Therefore, multiply £6,325 by 5.5370 to get £35,022. You then subtract the cost of the initial investment (£10,000) to obtain the net present value of £25,022.

5.7.5   Strengths and weaknesses

NPV has the following strengths and weaknesses:

Strengths

- It gives an absolute measure that immediately shows the change in shareholders' wealth due to an investment.
- It gives a clear accept/reject decision.
- It always gives the correct ranking for mutually exclusive projects.
- Changes in interest rates over time can easily be incorporated into NPV calculations.
- A modified form of NPV can be used in capital rationing situations.

Weaknesses

- It gives an absolute figure. Managers often find a capital return as a percentage more understandable, as they are able to relate it to current interest rates, etc.
- The future cash flows used can only be estimated and are not amounts known with certainty. (This is a limitation of all methods using future cash flows.)
- The discount rate is calculated using figures that are not known with certainty. (Calculation of the discount rate is beyond the scope of this module.)
- It is assumed that all cash flows other than the initial investment arise at the end of the year. This assumption will reduce accuracy.

5.8 Internal rate of return (IRR)

The **internal rate of return (IRR)** of a project is the discount rate which gives a zero NPV. The relationship between the NPV and IRR of a project can be shown diagrammatically.

The calculations in Figure 68 come from Section 5.8.1 'Method of calculation'.

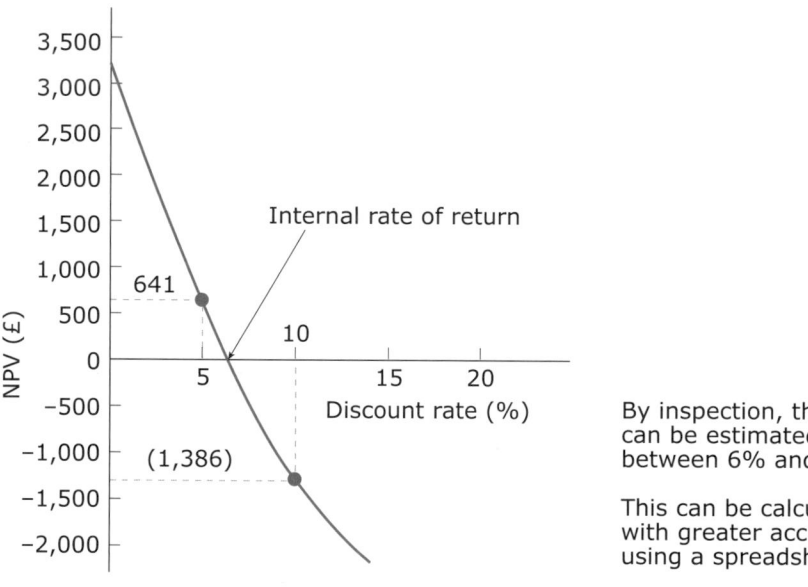

By inspection, the IRR can be estimated as between 6% and 7%.

This can be calculated with greater accuracy using a spreadsheet.

Figure 68   The relationship between NPV and IRR

The lower the discount rate, the lower will be its impact on the value of the cash flows over time. As a result, the lower the discount rate, the greater the present value of all future cash flows, and the higher the NPV.

Decision rule   A proposal with an IRR equal to or greater than the cost of capital (discount rate) can be accepted. If there is more than one choice of project, the project with the highest IRR should be accepted.

5.8.1   Method of calculation

IRR can be calculated manually using trial and error and linear interpolation.

Consider the following simplified example.

A company is considering purchasing a new machine. It is estimated that use of the new machine costing £24,000 will increase the company's cash inflows by:

	Year 1	Year 2	Year 3
Cash inflows (£)	10,000	10,000	7,000

To find the discount rate which gives a zero NPV, find two NPVs, one negative and one positive, and interpolate between the two results. (Two positives or two negatives could be used; in which case the calculation would differ slightly from the one explained below. This approach is not covered in this module.)

Trying 10%

Cash flow (£)	Year 0	Year 1	Year 2	Year 3
Purchase	(24,000)			
Cash inflows		10,000	10,000	7,000
Net cash flow	(24,000)	10,000	10,000	7,000
Discount factor 10%	1.0000	0.9091	0.8264	0.7513
Present value	(24,000)	9,091	8,264	5,259
NPV (negative)	(1,386)			

This gives a negative NPV of £1,386; so a positive NPV must be found. Try 5%, as the lower the discount rate, the less heavily future receipts are discounted.

Trying 5%

Cash flow (£)	Year 0	Year 1	Year 2	Year 3
Purchase	(24,000)			
Cash inflows		10,000	10,000	7,000
Net cash flow	(24,000)	10,000	10,000	7,000
Discount factor 5%	1.0000	0.9524	0.9070	0.8638
Present value	(24,000)	9,524	9,070	6,047
NPV (positive)	641			

Using a 10% discount rate gives a negative NPV, and using a discount rate of 5% gives a positive NPV. Therefore the IRR (discount rate that gives a zero NPV) must lie somewhere between 10% and 5%. The two discount rates and their NPVs can be used to calculate the IRR using interpolation.

The interpolation formula (see Figure 69 for definition of terms) is:

$$a + \left((b-a) \times \frac{NPVa}{NPVa - NPVb} \right) \text{ which gives}$$

$$5\% + \left((10-5) \times \frac{641}{641 - 1{,}386} \right) = 6.58\%$$

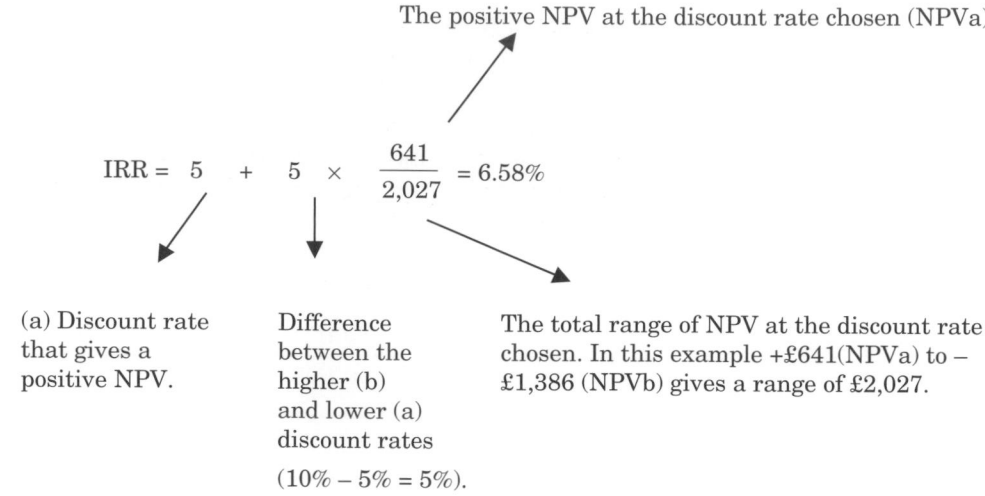

The positive NPV at the discount rate chosen (NPVa).

$$IRR = 5 + 5 \times \frac{641}{2{,}027} = 6.58\%$$

(a) Discount rate that gives a positive NPV.

Difference between the higher (b) and lower (a) discount rates (10% − 5% = 5%).

The total range of NPV at the discount rate chosen. In this example +£641(NPVa) to − £1,386 (NPVb) gives a range of £2,027.

Figure 69   IRR formula

Calculating an accurate IRR manually is fairly time-consuming. However, the calculation can be performed quickly using a spreadsheet.

Spreadsheet: calculating ARR, NPV and IRR

ARR, NPV and IRR can be calculated using a spreadsheet. For example:

	A	B	C	D	E	
1	**Investment appraisal**					
2						
3	Year	Cash flow		Depreciation	Profit	
4	0	(6,000)				
5	1	3,000		1,000	2,000	
6	2	2,000		1,000	1,000	
7	3	2,000		1,000	1,000	
8	4	2,000		1,000	1,000	
9	5	1,000		1,000	0	
10	6	1,000		1,000	0	
11						
12						
13	C of C	0.15		The spreadsheet formulae used are		
14	ARR	27.8%		= AVERAGE (E5:E10)/((6000+0)/2)*100 entered in cell B14		
15	NPV	+£1,509		= NPV(B13,B5:B10)+B4 entered in cell B15		
16	IRR	26%		= IRR(B4:B10,0.15) entered in cell B16		

Activity 5.4 ....

Section 5.7.4 looked at four projects and different NPVs were calculated using differing discount rates. All projects considered there have a positive NPV when discounting at 10%, but when discounting at 25%, we see that A would have an IRR of just over 25%, B would have an IRR of over 30% and C over 25% and D would have IRRs of between 10% and 25%.

Calculate the internal rates of return for projects A, B, C and D. Do it manually first, using interpolation, and then perform the same calculations using your spreadsheet. (You have already been given the IRR for project A but you may find it helpful to do it again in this exercise along with the others.) There is information on using spreadsheets in Session 6.

Feedback ....

Using a spreadsheet the results are as follows. Note that the spreadsheet calculates discount factors to six or seven decimal places.

	A	B	C	D	E	F	G	H	I
1	Year	Project A(£)		£		Year	Project B(£)		£
2	0	(20,000)	1.000000	(20,000)		0	(30,000)	1.0000000	(30,000)
3	1	0	0.792446	0		1	15,000	0.7522519	11,284
4	2	7,500	0.627971	4,710		2	15,000	0.5658829	8,488
5	3	0	0.497634	0		3	15,000	0.4256865	6,385
6	4	15,000	0.394348	5,915		4	12,000	0.3202234	3,843
7	5	30,000	0.3125	9,375		NPV			0
8	NPV			0		IRR		0.329342	
9	IRR		0.261915						
10									
11	Year	Project C (£)		£		Year	Project D (£)		£
12	0	(30,000)	1.000000	(30,000)		0	(40,000)	1.0000000	(40,000)
13	1	0	0.788774	0		1	5,000	0.8297292	4,149
14	2	20,000	0.622164	12,443		2	10,000	0.6884505	6,885
15	3	20,000	0.490747	9,815		3	15,000	0.5712275	8,568
16	4	20,000	0.387089	7,742		4	25,000	0.4739641	11,849
17	NPV			0		5	10,000	0.3932619	3,933
18	IRR		0.26779			6	10,000	0.3263008	3,263
19						7	5,000	0.2707413	1,354
20						NPV			0
21						IRR		0.2052125	

To one decimal place (for percentages), the IRRs are:

A = 26.2%, B = 32.9%, C = 26.8%, D = 20.5%.

You should now be more aware of the benefits of using a spreadsheet to perform IRR calculations: it is quicker than interpolation, and much more accurate.

5.8.2   The problem of multiple yields

If a project has more than one negative cash flow or cash flows arising after the initial cash outflow, that swing between positive and negative values means that there is likely to be more than one IRR or no IRR at all.

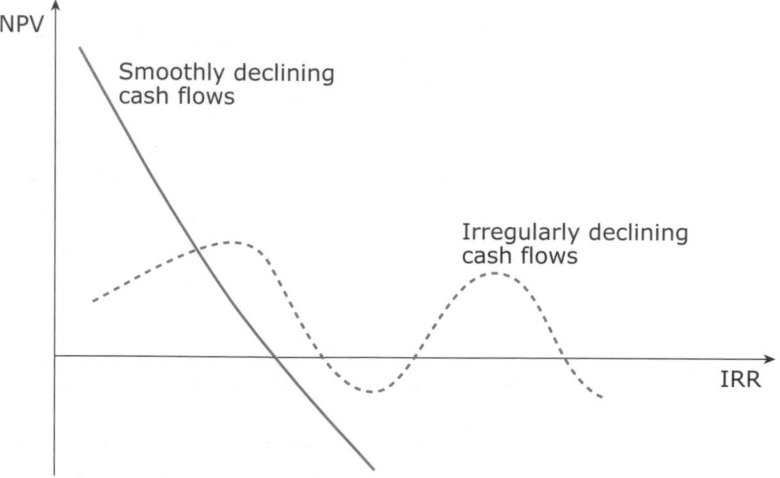

Figure 70   IRR and multiple yields

Typically, there will be a different IRR every time a cash flow changes 'sign' (i.e., from positive to negative or vice versa). However, some projects with cash flows that exhibit such changes will have no IRRs. This is a complex topic and is outside the scope of this module.

5.8.3   Mutually exclusive projects

Choosing between two mutually exclusive projects using the IRR decision rule can lead to an incorrect decision. For example:

Project	NPV at 10%	IRR
1	£604,000	14.17%
2	£443,000	15.75%

If the IRR method is used, then project 2 will be chosen, as it has the higher IRR of 15.75%. The NPV method with a discount rate of 10% favours project 1 because it has the higher NPV of £604,000, and according to general principles this is the one to choose.

5.8.4   Strengths and weaknesses

The IRR has the following strengths and weaknesses.

Strengths

- It is readily understood by managers who are familiar with the idea of considering percentage returns from projects.
- Using the IRR prevents a need for total accuracy in estimating the cost of capital, as the IRR gives a discount rate below which the investment/project gives a positive return and above which the investment/project gives a negative return (see Figure 68).

Weaknesses

- It gives no impression of the scale of the project. For example, a project having cash inflows and outflows in hundreds of pounds (£'00) with an IRR of 20% would be considered superior to one with cash inflows and outflows of millions of pounds (£'000,000) with an IRR of 10%.

- If a project has more than one negative cash flow, it can have more than one IRR or no IRR at all.
- The IRR makes the implicit assumption that all proceeds from a project can be instantly invested to earn a return equal to the IRR of the original project, that is, that every penny of revenue is *immediately* invested at a rate of return *equal* to the IRR. This is a potentially fatal flaw in the IRR, particularly with respect to capital investment projects that earn higher than normal returns.

5.9 Relevant costs and revenues

Payback, NPV and IRR are all calculated from incremental cash flows. For a cost or revenue to be relevant to the capital investment decision and therefore to justify inclusion in payback, NPV and IRR calculations, it must have the following characteristics.

- *It must be a cash flow.* Accounting entries for items such as depreciation are not cash flows, but accounting adjustments that spread costs over the life of the asset.
- *It must be incremental.* The cash flows must arise directly as a result of the decision to undertake the project.
- *It must arise in the future.* Past costs (known as **sunk costs**) have already arisen and are therefore irrelevant to future decision making and should be ignored. For example, materials in inventory that were purchased before the project was started and which cannot be used elsewhere other than in the project are a sunk cost and should not be included in the payback, NPV and IRR calculations. Other examples might include market surveys completed prior to the start of the project or assets such as land and machinery purchased prior to the start of the project, which will be used in the project.

5.9.1 Changes in working capital

One relevant cost that must not be overlooked is any additional (or reduction in) *working capital* needed if a project is undertaken. If an organisation invests in a new machine that is forecast to increase sales volume by 10%, it will need to be able to fund the increased working capital elements. The increase in sales will require:

- an increase in inventory (raw materials, work-in-progress and finished goods)
- a related increase in creditors (or trade payables that will reduce working capital required)
- an increase in debtors (or trade receivables).

The amount of working capital required is often significant in relation to the project's overall outlay. Failing to include this in the appraisal calculation can seriously distort the cash flow forecasts and, hence, the financial appraisal. Where possible, this working capital should be built into the cash flow computation.

Here is another example. Otter Stationery is considering bidding for a new contract to print specialised forms. The management accountant has identified the following information.

- The contract is for a period of five years.
- Revenues will be £2.5 million a year and operating costs (excluding depreciation) are expected to be £1.4 million.
- A new machine is required, which will cost £3.2 million and which is expected to be sold for £750,000 at the end of the contract period.
- A full year's inventory of paper (costing £1.2 million) needs to be purchased before any sales can be made. One year's inventory of paper will be held during the life of the project. Other inventory purchases are included in the operating costs above.
- Working capital of £500,000 will be needed in year 1. It will be recovered at the end of year 5.
- The cost of capital is 10% per annum.

	Time					
	0	**1**	**2**	**3**	**4**	**5**
	£'000	£'000	£'000	£'000	£'000	£'000
Investment cash flows						
New machine	(3,200)					750
Inventory	(1,200)					1,200
Other working capital		(500)				500
Total	(4,400)	(500)				2,450
Operating cash flows						
Revenue		2,500	2,500	2,500	2,500	2,500
Expenditure		(1,400)	(1,400)	(1,400)	(1,400)	(1,400)
Total		1,100	1,100	1,100	1,100	1,100
Net cash flow	(4,400)	600	1,100	1,100	1,100	3,550
Discount factor 10%	1.0000	0.9091	0.8264	0.7513	0.6830	0.6209
Present value	(4,400)	545	909	826	751	2,204
NPV	**+835**					

5.9.2 Relevant material costs

Consider the following example.

Ridge Manufacturing Ltd is considering a two year contract. The annual raw material requirement is as follows:

Raw material	W	X	Y	Z
Current inventory level (units)	–	50	100	100
Annual requirement (units)	10	200	25	40
Original cost of inventory (£ per unit)	–	75	75	30
Current purchase price (£ per unit)	40	80	80	30
Scrap value (£ per unit)	25	10	30	20
Alternative use in the company	Yes	Yes	No	Yes
Contribution earned on alternative use (£ per unit, before material cost)	45	100	–	52

Assume that purchases are paid for at the end of the year in which delivery takes place. Any inventory that is scrapped will generate immediate proceeds. Owing to supplier problems, no purchases of material Z are possible in the first year of the project.

In determining the appropriate costs to include for the four different material types, the three criteria stated above must be considered, namely, the cost must be an incremental or future cash flow.

Material W

None is currently in inventory and therefore in taking on a new project the business will need to buy in raw material each year. The relevant cost is therefore the current purchase price of £40 per unit.

Material X

There are already 50 units in inventory. The original purchase price is irrelevant as it is a sunk cost. The incremental cost to the company of using the 50 units in the new project must therefore be determined. Material X is used elsewhere in the business. Therefore, if 50 units are used on the new project, another part of the business will need to buy extra units at the current purchase price of £80. As the material can be readily purchased, the situation is identical to material W, as the relevant cost for all units of X is the current purchase price of £80.

Material Y

There is more inventory of Y than will be required to satisfy the two years of production of the new product. The question therefore is: what would have happened to the material if it was not used in the new project? The material is not used elsewhere in the business and so no additional replacement purchases are required, hence the only options would be to keep it for no purpose or to sell it as scrap. In using it in this project, the business is therefore losing the opportunity of selling it for £30 a unit. The relevant cost, in this case the **opportunity cost**, is the £30 income per unit foregone from the sale as scrap.

Material Z

This is similar to material X in that it is in inventory and used elsewhere in the business. If 40 units are used in year 1, another part of the business would need to buy in extra units at the current purchase price of £30. However, as the material cannot be easily purchased the situation is therefore more difficult. If the business uses these units of material Z in year 1, the production of other products will be prevented. The relevant cost for that first year is therefore the lost contribution from the abandoned production elsewhere in the factory of £52 per unit. In year 2 there is no longer a problem in replacing the material and so the relevant cost for year 2 will be the current purchase price of £30.

Material	Relevant cash flows (£)		
	Year 0	Year 1	Year 2
W		£40 × 10 = £400	£40 × 10 = £400
X		£80 × 200 = £16,000	£80 × 200 = £16,000
Y	£30 × 25 × 2 = £1,500		
Z		£52 × 40 = £2,080	£30 × 40 = £1,200

Activity 5.5   ....

Find out which capital investment appraisal procedures are used in your organisation (or in one about which you can obtain information), and why.

What would your B292 studies indicate to you about the appropriateness of the approach taken?

Spend about 25 minutes doing this.

Feedback   ....

It is important that you consider the choice in the light of the material you have studied in this unit, not just the techniques themselves, but also the non-financial factors that impinge upon and affect the capital investment appraisal decision making process.

5.10 Practical considerations in capital investment appraisal

Payback, NPV and IRR assume that it is possible to quantify the cash flow effects of investment.

5.10.1 Problems and risk

As capital investments are long-term investments, it is not always easy to quantify the cash inflows and outflows. The further the period of the cash flow is away from the initial capital outflow, the more difficult it may be to estimate figures. Moreover, problems arise with strategic investment projects, such as the development of new products or the takeover of another business. Such projects present some intricate problems. These are listed below.

- The hurdle rate (cost of capital/discount rate). How will the appropriate discount rate be selected?

- The rate and pattern of growth that will be forecast. Can future revenues and costs be forecast with reasonable accuracy? Will high volumes reduce unit costs? Will competitor action reduce prices?

The risks inherent in a project are often unknown. They may, for example, arise from economic, technological, political, competitive, legislative sources, etc. There are several questions which should be asked. For example, how accurate are the estimated figures? How successful will the product or service produced be? When the risks inherent in the project are unknown, many organisations require a project to clear the hurdle rate by a significant margin. Remember, one of the assumptions inherent in using the cost of capital as the discount rate is that the project appraised has the same degree of risk as the company is currently undertaking across all its projects. By setting a hurdle rate higher than the cost of capital, organisations hope to minimise the chance of taking on a loss-making project.

In practice, the effect of this risk application is that an organisation with a cost of capital of 10% may apply a much higher hurdle rate, say 20%, to a project with a very significant perceived risk. As all strategic and long-term projects contain risks such as those discussed above, a risk-averse approach serves to limit acceptance of projects of this type. Yet it is precisely this type of project that must be considered if organisations are to grow and remain competitive in the market place.

Sensitivity analysis could be applied to capital investment appraisal and a range of probabilities assigned to the events. Sensitivity analysis is a modelling procedure used in forecasting whereby changes are made in the estimates of the variables (e.g., component costs, sales volume, discount rate, tax rate) to establish whether any will critically affect the outcome of the forecast. So it asks 'what if' questions. It can easily be performed using spreadsheets. Without sensitivity analysis, no information will be available as to the risk associated with a project. If there is a wide margin of safety, the organisation can be fairly confident that the project will give a satisfactory return (even if the incremental cash flows are significantly different from those forecast). If, however, the margin of safety is narrow, more investigation is needed. A project that looks risky could be rejected even if it has a positive NPV or a higher IRR than the hurdle rate.

5.10.2   The impact of non-financial factors

The quantitative appraisal of a project is just part of the organisational process. Managers are guided by organisational objectives and are unable to base their decisions solely on financial data. It is imperative that, before a project proposal advances towards the point of sanctioning and implementation, other factors, such as those listed below, should be considered.

- The market. For example, is the investment needed as part of a change in the market strategy of the organisation?
- The environment. For example, will the investment or one of the other possible options under consideration lead to less noise in the geographical area affected?
- Competitors. For example, what effect will each option under consideration have on the long-term competitiveness of the business?

- Staff resources. For example, will the organisation need to buy in skills to make the product produced by one of the new machines under consideration?
- Legal obligations. For example, the project may be important, as it allows the organisation to comply with health and safety legislation.

Success in having a project approved will depend on how the project is put to, and received by, senior managers. They may well not trust the figures, believing them to be open to manipulation. They expect projects to have positive NPVs or to be convincing in other ways; otherwise they would not have been put forward to them.

Summary

This session looked at the difference between simple and compound interest. Simple interest accrues on the principal, whereas compound interest accrues on the principal plus the interest reinvested. Both look forward in time to a future date. Discounting was used to calculate the present value of a future sum of money.

Then the session looked at ARR, payback, NPV and IRR, the four most common capital investment appraisal techniques used to apply financial criteria to long-term project proposals and calculate their economic viability. ARR is calculated using profits, whereas payback, NPV and IRR are calculated using expected future cash flows. There was also discussion about which costs are relevant and which irrelevant in decision making. The strengths and limitations of each of the four methods were identified.

Some of the practical issues that surround the capital investment decision process were explained. It is important never to overlook the inherent flaws in any long-term forecasting method: the aim is to attach *exact accounting numbers to uncertain future events*. However, the impact of non-financial factors in the decision making process should not be overlooked.

Session 6 looks at spreadsheets, including the construction of multi-sheet spreadsheets.

Table 1

Present value of 1 at compound interest: $(1 + r)^{-n}$

Interest rate (%)

n	1	2	3	4	5	6	7	8	9	10	11	12	13	14	15	16	17	18	19	20	21	22	23	24	25
1	0.9901	0.9804	0.9709	0.9615	0.9524	0.9434	0.9346	0.9259	0.9174	0.9091	0.9009	0.8929	0.8850	0.8772	0.8696	0.8621	0.8547	0.8475	0.8403	0.8333	0.8264	0.8197	0.8130	0.8065	0.8000
2	0.9803	0.9612	0.9426	0.9246	0.9070	0.8900	0.8734	0.8573	0.8417	0.8264	0.8116	0.7972	0.7831	0.7695	0.7561	0.7432	0.7305	0.7182	0.7062	0.6944	0.6830	0.6719	0.6610	0.6504	0.6400
3	0.9706	0.9423	0.9151	0.8890	0.8638	0.8396	0.8163	0.7938	0.7722	0.7513	0.7312	0.7118	0.6931	0.6750	0.6575	0.6407	0.6244	0.6086	0.5934	0.5787	0.5645	0.5507	0.5374	0.5245	0.5120
4	0.9610	0.9238	0.8885	0.8548	0.8227	0.7921	0.7629	0.7350	0.7084	0.6830	0.6587	0.6355	0.6133	0.5921	0.5718	0.5523	0.5337	0.5158	0.4987	0.4823	0.4665	0.4514	0.4369	0.4230	0.4096
5	0.9515	0.9057	0.8626	0.8219	0.7835	0.7473	0.7130	0.6806	0.6499	0.6209	0.5935	0.5674	0.5428	0.5194	0.4972	0.4761	0.4561	0.4371	0.4190	0.4019	0.3855	0.3700	0.3552	0.3411	0.3277
6	0.9420	0.8880	0.8375	0.7903	0.7462	0.7050	0.6663	0.6302	0.5963	0.5645	0.5346	0.5066	0.4803	0.4556	0.4323	0.4104	0.3898	0.3704	0.3521	0.3349	0.3186	0.3033	0.2888	0.2751	0.2621
7	0.9327	0.8706	0.8131	0.7599	0.7107	0.6651	0.6227	0.5835	0.5470	0.5132	0.4817	0.4523	0.4251	0.3996	0.3759	0.3538	0.3332	0.3139	0.2959	0.2791	0.2633	0.2486	0.2348	0.2218	0.2097
8	0.9235	0.8535	0.7894	0.7307	0.6768	0.6274	0.5820	0.5403	0.5019	0.4665	0.4339	0.4039	0.3762	0.3506	0.3269	0.3050	0.2848	0.2660	0.2487	0.2326	0.2176	0.2038	0.1909	0.1789	0.1678
9	0.9143	0.8368	0.7664	0.7026	0.6446	0.5919	0.5439	0.5002	0.4604	0.4241	0.3909	0.3606	0.3329	0.3075	0.2843	0.2630	0.2434	0.2255	0.2090	0.1938	0.1799	0.1670	0.1552	0.1443	0.1342
10	0.9053	0.8203	0.7441	0.6756	0.6139	0.5584	0.5083	0.4632	0.4224	0.3855	0.3522	0.3220	0.2946	0.2697	0.2472	0.2267	0.2080	0.1911	0.1756	0.1615	0.1486	0.1369	0.1262	0.1164	0.1074
11	0.8963	0.8043	0.7224	0.6496	0.5847	0.5268	0.4751	0.4289	0.3875	0.3505	0.3173	0.2875	0.2607	0.2366	0.2149	0.1954	0.1778	0.1619	0.1476	0.1346	0.1228	0.1122	0.1026	0.0938	0.0859
12	0.8874	0.7885	0.7014	0.6246	0.5568	0.4970	0.4440	0.3971	0.3555	0.3186	0.2858	0.2567	0.2307	0.2076	0.1869	0.1685	0.1520	0.1372	0.1240	0.1122	0.1015	0.0920	0.0834	0.0757	0.0687
13	0.8787	0.7730	0.6810	0.6006	0.5303	0.4688	0.4150	0.3677	0.3262	0.2897	0.2575	0.2292	0.2042	0.1821	0.1625	0.1452	0.1299	0.1163	0.1042	0.0935	0.0839	0.0754	0.0678	0.0610	0.0550
14	0.8700	0.7579	0.6611	0.5775	0.5051	0.4423	0.3878	0.3405	0.2992	0.2633	0.2320	0.2046	0.1807	0.1597	0.1413	0.1252	0.1110	0.0985	0.0876	0.0779	0.0693	0.0618	0.0551	0.0492	0.0440
15	0.8613	0.7430	0.6419	0.5553	0.4810	0.4173	0.3624	0.3152	0.2745	0.2394	0.2090	0.1827	0.1599	0.1401	0.1229	0.1079	0.0949	0.0835	0.0736	0.0649	0.0573	0.0507	0.0448	0.0397	0.0352
16	0.8528	0.7284	0.6232	0.5339	0.4581	0.3936	0.3387	0.2919	0.2519	0.2176	0.1883	0.1631	0.1415	0.1229	0.1069	0.0930	0.0811	0.0708	0.0618	0.0541	0.0474	0.0415	0.0364	0.0320	0.0281
17	0.8444	0.7142	0.6050	0.5134	0.4363	0.3714	0.3166	0.2703	0.2311	0.1978	0.1696	0.1456	0.1252	0.1078	0.0929	0.0802	0.0693	0.0600	0.0520	0.0451	0.0391	0.0340	0.0296	0.0258	0.0225
18	0.8360	0.7002	0.5874	0.4936	0.4155	0.3503	0.2959	0.2502	0.2120	0.1799	0.1528	0.1300	0.1108	0.0946	0.0808	0.0691	0.0592	0.0508	0.0437	0.0376	0.0323	0.0279	0.0241	0.0208	0.0180
19	0.8277	0.6864	0.5703	0.4746	0.3957	0.3305	0.2765	0.2317	0.1945	0.1635	0.1377	0.1161	0.0981	0.0829	0.0703	0.0596	0.0506	0.0431	0.0367	0.0313	0.0267	0.0229	0.0196	0.0168	0.0144
20	0.8195	0.6730	0.5537	0.4564	0.3769	0.3118	0.2584	0.2145	0.1784	0.1486	0.1240	0.1037	0.0868	0.0728	0.0611	0.0514	0.0433	0.0365	0.0308	0.0261	0.0221	0.0187	0.0159	0.0135	0.0115
21	0.8114	0.6598	0.5375	0.4388	0.3589	0.2942	0.2415	0.1987	0.1637	0.1351	0.1117	0.0926	0.0768	0.0638	0.0531	0.0443	0.0370	0.0309	0.0259	0.0217	0.0183	0.0154	0.0129	0.0109	0.0092
22	0.8034	0.6468	0.5219	0.4220	0.3418	0.2775	0.2257	0.1839	0.1502	0.1228	0.1007	0.0826	0.0680	0.0560	0.0462	0.0382	0.0316	0.0262	0.0218	0.0183	0.0151	0.0126	0.0105	0.0088	0.0074
23	0.7954	0.6342	0.5067	0.4057	0.3256	0.2618	0.2109	0.1703	0.1378	0.1117	0.0907	0.0738	0.0601	0.0491	0.0402	0.0329	0.0270	0.0222	0.0183	0.0151	0.0125	0.0103	0.0086	0.0071	0.0059
24	0.7876	0.6217	0.4919	0.3901	0.3101	0.2470	0.1971	0.1577	0.1264	0.1015	0.0817	0.0659	0.0532	0.0431	0.0349	0.0284	0.0231	0.0188	0.0154	0.0126	0.0103	0.0085	0.0070	0.0057	0.0047
25	0.7798	0.6095	0.4776	0.3751	0.2953	0.2330	0.1842	0.1460	0.1160	0.0923	0.0736	0.0588	0.0471	0.0378	0.0304	0.0245	0.0197	0.0160	0.0129	0.0105	0.0085	0.0069	0.0057	0.0046	0.0038
26	0.7720	0.5976	0.4637	0.3607	0.2812	0.2198	0.1722	0.1352	0.1064	0.0839	0.0663	0.0525	0.0417	0.0331	0.0264	0.0211	0.0169	0.0135	0.0109	0.0087	0.0070	0.0057	0.0046	0.0037	0.0030
27	0.7644	0.5859	0.4502	0.3468	0.2678	0.2074	0.1609	0.1252	0.0976	0.0763	0.0597	0.0469	0.0369	0.0291	0.0230	0.0182	0.0144	0.0115	0.0091	0.0073	0.0058	0.0047	0.0037	0.0030	0.0024
28	0.7568	0.5744	0.4371	0.3335	0.2551	0.1956	0.1504	0.1159	0.0895	0.0693	0.0538	0.0419	0.0326	0.0255	0.0200	0.0157	0.0123	0.0097	0.0077	0.0061	0.0048	0.0038	0.0030	0.0024	0.0019
29	0.7493	0.5631	0.4243	0.3207	0.2429	0.1846	0.1406	0.1073	0.0822	0.0630	0.0485	0.0374	0.0289	0.0224	0.0174	0.0135	0.0105	0.0082	0.0064	0.0051	0.0040	0.0031	0.0025	0.0020	0.0015
30	0.7419	0.5521	0.4120	0.3083	0.2314	0.1741	0.1314	0.0994	0.0754	0.0573	0.0437	0.0334	0.0256	0.0196	0.0151	0.0116	0.0090	0.0070	0.0054	0.0042	0.0033	0.0026	0.0020	0.0016	0.0012
31	0.7346	0.5412	0.4000	0.2965	0.2204	0.1643	0.1228	0.0920	0.0691	0.0521	0.0394	0.0298	0.0226	0.0172	0.0131	0.0100	0.0077	0.0059	0.0046	0.0035	0.0027	0.0021	0.0016	0.0013	0.0010
32	0.7273	0.5306	0.3883	0.2851	0.2099	0.1550	0.1147	0.0852	0.0634	0.0474	0.0355	0.0266	0.0200	0.0151	0.0114	0.0087	0.0066	0.0050	0.0038	0.0029	0.0022	0.0017	0.0013	0.0010	0.0008
33	0.7201	0.5202	0.3770	0.2741	0.1999	0.1462	0.1072	0.0789	0.0582	0.0431	0.0319	0.0238	0.0177	0.0132	0.0099	0.0075	0.0056	0.0042	0.0032	0.0024	0.0019	0.0014	0.0011	0.0008	0.0006
34	0.7130	0.5100	0.3660	0.2636	0.1904	0.1379	0.1002	0.0730	0.0534	0.0391	0.0288	0.0212	0.0157	0.0116	0.0086	0.0064	0.0048	0.0036	0.0027	0.0020	0.0015	0.0012	0.0009	0.0007	0.0005
35	0.7059	0.5000	0.3554	0.2534	0.1813	0.1301	0.0937	0.0676	0.0490	0.0356	0.0259	0.0189	0.0139	0.0102	0.0075	0.0055	0.0041	0.0030	0.0023	0.0017	0.0013	0.0009	0.0007	0.0005	0.0004
36	0.6989	0.4902	0.3450	0.2437	0.1727	0.1227	0.0875	0.0626	0.0449	0.0323	0.0234	0.0169	0.0123	0.0089	0.0065	0.0048	0.0035	0.0026	0.0019	0.0014	0.0010	0.0008	0.0006	0.0004	0.0003
37	0.6920	0.4806	0.3350	0.2343	0.1644	0.1158	0.0818	0.0580	0.0412	0.0294	0.0210	0.0151	0.0109	0.0078	0.0057	0.0041	0.0030	0.0022	0.0016	0.0012	0.0009	0.0006	0.0005	0.0003	0.0003
38	0.6852	0.4712	0.3252	0.2253	0.1566	0.1092	0.0765	0.0537	0.0378	0.0267	0.0190	0.0135	0.0096	0.0069	0.0049	0.0036	0.0026	0.0019	0.0013	0.0010	0.0007	0.0005	0.0004	0.0003	0.0002
39	0.6784	0.4619	0.3158	0.2166	0.1491	0.1031	0.0715	0.0497	0.0347	0.0243	0.0171	0.0120	0.0085	0.0060	0.0043	0.0031	0.0022	0.0016	0.0011	0.0008	0.0006	0.0004	0.0003	0.0002	0.0002
40	0.6717	0.4529	0.3066	0.2083	0.1420	0.0972	0.0668	0.0460	0.0318	0.0221	0.0154	0.0107	0.0075	0.0053	0.0037	0.0026	0.0019	0.0013	0.0010	0.0007	0.0005	0.0004	0.0003	0.0002	0.0001

Periods

Table 2

Present value of an annuity of 1: $\frac{1-(1+r)^{-n}}{r}$

Interest rate (%)

n	1	2	3	4	5	6	7	8	9	10	11	12	13	14	15	16	17	18	19	20	21	22	23	24	25
1	0.9901	0.9804	0.9709	0.9615	0.9524	0.9434	0.9346	0.9259	0.9174	0.9091	0.9009	0.8929	0.8850	0.8772	0.8696	0.8621	0.8547	0.8475	0.8403	0.8333	0.8264	0.8197	0.8130	0.8065	0.8000
2	1.9704	1.9416	1.9135	1.8861	1.8594	1.8334	1.8080	1.7833	1.7591	1.7355	1.7125	1.6901	1.6681	1.6467	1.6257	1.6052	1.5852	1.5656	1.5465	1.5278	1.5095	1.4915	1.4740	1.4568	1.4400
3	2.9410	2.8839	2.8286	2.7751	2.7232	2.6730	2.6243	2.5771	2.5313	2.4869	2.4437	2.4018	2.3612	2.3216	2.2832	2.2459	2.2096	2.1743	2.1399	2.1065	2.0739	2.0422	2.0114	1.9813	1.9520
4	3.9020	3.8077	3.7171	3.6299	3.5460	3.4651	3.3872	3.3121	3.2397	3.1699	3.1024	3.0373	2.9745	2.9137	2.8550	2.7982	2.7432	2.6901	2.6386	2.5887	2.5404	2.4936	2.4483	2.4043	2.3616
5	4.8534	4.7135	4.5797	4.4518	4.3295	4.2124	4.1002	3.9927	3.8897	3.7908	3.6959	3.6048	3.5172	3.4331	3.3522	3.2743	3.1993	3.1272	3.0576	2.9906	2.9260	2.8636	2.8035	2.7454	2.6893
6	5.7955	5.6014	5.4172	5.2421	5.0757	4.9173	4.7665	4.6229	4.4859	4.3553	4.2305	4.1114	3.9975	3.8887	3.7845	3.6847	3.5892	3.4976	3.4098	3.3255	3.2446	3.1669	3.0923	3.0205	2.9514
7	6.7282	6.4720	6.2303	6.0021	5.7864	5.5824	5.3893	5.2064	5.0330	4.8684	4.7122	4.5638	4.4226	4.2883	4.1604	4.0386	3.9224	3.8115	3.7057	3.6046	3.5079	3.4155	3.3270	3.2423	3.1611
8	7.6517	7.3255	7.0197	6.7327	6.4632	6.2098	5.9713	5.7466	5.5348	5.3349	5.1461	4.9676	4.7988	4.6389	4.4873	4.3436	4.2072	4.0776	3.9544	3.8372	3.7256	3.6193	3.5179	3.4212	3.3289
9	8.5660	8.1622	7.7861	7.4353	7.1078	6.8017	6.5152	6.2469	5.9952	5.7590	5.5370	5.3282	5.1317	4.9464	4.7716	4.6065	4.4506	4.3030	4.1633	4.0310	3.9054	3.7863	3.6731	3.5655	3.4631
10	9.4713	8.9826	8.5302	8.1109	7.7217	7.3601	7.0236	6.7101	6.4177	6.1446	5.8892	5.6502	5.4262	5.2161	5.0188	4.8332	4.6586	4.4941	4.3389	4.1925	4.0541	3.9232	3.7993	3.6819	3.5705
11	10.3676	9.7868	9.2526	8.7605	8.3064	7.8869	7.4987	7.1390	6.8052	6.4951	6.2065	5.9377	5.6869	5.4527	5.2337	5.0286	4.8364	4.6560	4.4865	4.3271	4.1769	4.0354	3.9018	3.7757	3.6564
12	11.2551	10.5753	9.9540	9.3851	8.8633	8.3838	7.9427	7.5361	7.1607	6.8137	6.4924	6.1944	5.9176	5.6603	5.4206	5.1971	4.9884	4.7932	4.6105	4.4392	4.2784	4.1274	3.9852	3.8514	3.7251
13	12.1337	11.3484	10.6350	9.9856	9.3936	8.8527	8.3577	7.9038	7.4869	7.1034	6.7499	6.4235	6.1218	5.8424	5.5831	5.3423	5.1183	4.9095	4.7147	4.5327	4.3624	4.2028	4.0530	3.9124	3.7801
14	13.0037	12.1062	11.2961	10.5631	9.8986	9.2950	8.7455	8.2442	7.7862	7.3667	6.9819	6.6282	6.3025	6.0021	5.7245	5.4675	5.2293	5.0081	4.8023	4.6106	4.4317	4.2646	4.1082	3.9616	3.8241
15	13.8651	12.8493	11.9379	11.1184	10.3797	9.7122	9.1079	8.5595	8.0607	7.6061	7.1909	6.8109	6.4624	6.1422	5.8474	5.5755	5.3242	5.0916	4.8759	4.6755	4.4890	4.3152	4.1530	4.0013	3.8593
16	14.7179	13.5777	12.5611	11.6523	10.8378	10.1059	9.4466	8.8514	8.3126	7.8237	7.3792	6.9740	6.6039	6.2651	5.9542	5.6685	5.4053	5.1624	4.9377	4.7296	4.5364	4.3567	4.1894	4.0333	3.8874
17	15.5623	14.2919	13.1661	12.1657	11.2741	10.4773	9.7632	9.1216	8.5436	8.0216	7.5488	7.1196	6.7291	6.3729	6.0472	5.7487	5.4746	5.2223	4.9897	4.7746	4.5755	4.3908	4.2190	4.0591	3.9099
18	16.3983	14.9920	13.7535	12.6593	11.6896	10.8276	10.0591	9.3719	8.7556	8.2014	7.7016	7.2497	6.8399	6.4674	6.1280	5.8178	5.5339	5.2732	5.0333	4.8122	4.6079	4.4187	4.2431	4.0799	3.9279
19	17.2260	15.6785	14.3238	13.1339	12.0853	11.1581	10.3356	9.6036	8.9501	8.3649	7.8393	7.3658	6.9380	6.5504	6.1982	5.8775	5.5845	5.3162	5.0700	4.8435	4.6346	4.4415	4.2627	4.0967	3.9424
20	18.0456	16.3514	14.8775	13.5903	12.4622	11.4699	10.5940	9.8181	9.1285	8.5136	7.9633	7.4694	7.0248	6.6231	6.2593	5.9288	5.6278	5.3527	5.1009	4.8696	4.6567	4.4603	4.2786	4.1103	3.9539
21	18.8570	17.0112	15.4150	14.0292	12.8212	11.7641	10.8355	10.0168	9.2922	8.6487	8.0751	7.5620	7.1016	6.6870	6.3125	5.9731	5.6648	5.3837	5.1268	4.8913	4.6750	4.4756	4.2916	4.1212	3.9631
22	19.6604	17.6580	15.9369	14.4511	13.1630	12.0416	11.0612	10.2007	9.4424	8.7715	8.1757	7.6446	7.1695	6.7429	6.3587	6.0113	5.6964	5.4099	5.1486	4.9094	4.6900	4.4882	4.3021	4.1300	3.9705
23	20.4558	18.2922	16.4436	14.8568	13.4886	12.3034	11.2722	10.3711	9.5802	8.8832	8.2664	7.7184	7.2297	6.7921	6.3988	6.0442	5.7234	5.4321	5.1668	4.9245	4.7025	4.4985	4.3106	4.1371	3.9764
24	21.2434	18.9139	16.9355	15.2470	13.7986	12.5504	11.4693	10.5288	9.7066	8.9847	8.3481	7.7843	7.2829	6.8351	6.4338	6.0726	5.7465	5.4509	5.1822	4.9371	4.7128	4.5070	4.3176	4.1428	3.9811
25	22.0232	19.5235	17.4131	15.6221	14.0939	12.7834	11.6536	10.6748	9.8226	9.0770	8.4217	7.8431	7.3300	6.8729	6.4641	6.0971	5.7662	5.4669	5.1951	4.9476	4.7213	4.5139	4.3232	4.1474	3.9849
26	22.7952	20.1210	17.8768	15.9828	14.3752	13.0032	11.8258	10.8100	9.9290	9.1609	8.4881	7.8957	7.3717	6.9061	6.4906	6.1182	5.7831	5.4804	5.2060	4.9563	4.7284	4.5196	4.3278	4.1511	3.9879
27	23.5596	20.7069	18.3270	16.3296	14.6430	13.2105	11.9867	10.9352	10.0266	9.2372	8.5478	7.9426	7.4086	6.9352	6.5135	6.1364	5.7975	5.4919	5.2151	4.9636	4.7342	4.5243	4.3316	4.1542	3.9903
28	24.3164	21.2813	18.7641	16.6631	14.8981	13.4062	12.1371	11.0511	10.1161	9.3066	8.6016	7.9844	7.4412	6.9607	6.5335	6.1520	5.8099	5.5016	5.2228	4.9697	4.7390	4.5281	4.3346	4.1566	3.9923
29	25.0658	21.8444	19.1885	16.9837	15.1411	13.5907	12.2777	11.1584	10.1983	9.3696	8.6501	8.0218	7.4701	6.9830	6.5509	6.1656	5.8204	5.5098	5.2292	4.9747	4.7430	4.5312	4.3371	4.1585	3.9938
30	25.8077	22.3965	19.6004	17.2920	15.3725	13.7648	12.4090	11.2578	10.2737	9.4269	8.6938	8.0552	7.4957	7.0027	6.5660	6.1772	5.8294	5.5168	5.2347	4.9789	4.7463	4.5338	4.3391	4.1601	3.9950
31	26.5423	22.9377	20.0004	17.5885	15.5928	13.9291	12.5318	11.3498	10.3428	9.4790	8.7331	8.0850	7.5183	7.0199	6.5791	6.1872	5.8371	5.5227	5.2392	4.9824	4.7490	4.5359	4.3407	4.1614	3.9960
32	27.2696	23.4683	20.3888	17.8736	15.8027	14.0840	12.6466	11.4350	10.4062	9.5264	8.7686	8.1116	7.5383	7.0350	6.5905	6.1959	5.8437	5.5277	5.2430	4.9854	4.7512	4.5376	4.3421	4.1624	3.9968
33	27.9897	23.9886	20.7658	18.1476	16.0025	14.2302	12.7538	11.5139	10.4644	9.5694	8.8005	8.1354	7.5560	7.0482	6.6005	6.2034	5.8493	5.5320	5.2462	4.9878	4.7531	4.5390	4.3431	4.1632	3.9975
34	28.7027	24.4986	21.1318	18.4112	16.1929	14.3681	12.8540	11.5869	10.5178	9.6086	8.8293	8.1566	7.5717	7.0599	6.6091	6.2098	5.8541	5.5356	5.2489	4.9898	4.7546	4.5402	4.3440	4.1639	3.9980
35	29.4086	24.9986	21.4872	18.6646	16.3742	14.4982	12.9477	11.6546	10.5668	9.6442	8.8552	8.1755	7.5856	7.0700	6.6166	6.2153	5.8582	5.5386	5.2512	4.9915	4.7559	4.5411	4.3447	4.1644	3.9984
36	30.1075	25.4888	21.8323	18.9083	16.5469	14.6210	13.0352	11.7172	10.6118	9.6765	8.8786	8.1924	7.5979	7.0790	6.6231	6.2201	5.8617	5.5412	5.2531	4.9929	4.7569	4.5419	4.3453	4.1649	3.9987
37	30.7995	25.9695	22.1672	19.1426	16.7113	14.7368	13.1170	11.7752	10.6530	9.7059	8.8996	8.2075	7.6087	7.0868	6.6288	6.2242	5.8647	5.5434	5.2547	4.9941	4.7578	4.5426	4.3458	4.1652	3.9990
38	31.4847	26.4406	22.4925	19.3679	16.8679	14.8460	13.1935	11.8289	10.6908	9.7327	8.9186	8.2210	7.6183	7.0937	6.6338	6.2278	5.8673	5.5452	5.2561	4.9951	4.7585	4.5431	4.3462	4.1655	3.9992
39	32.1630	26.9026	22.8082	19.5845	17.0170	14.9491	13.2649	11.8786	10.7255	9.7570	8.9357	8.2330	7.6268	7.0997	6.6380	6.2309	5.8695	5.5468	5.2572	4.9959	4.7591	4.5435	4.3465	4.1657	3.9993
40	32.8347	27.3555	23.1148	19.7928	17.1591	15.0463	13.3317	11.9246	10.7574	9.7791	8.9511	8.2438	7.6344	7.1050	6.6418	6.2335	5.8713	5.5482	5.2582	4.9966	4.7596	4.5439	4.3467	4.1659	3.9995

Periods

SESSION **6 The role of spreadsheets in accounting**

Introduction

Upon completion of Session 6, you are expected to be able to:

- understand and explain the nature, benefits and limitations of spreadsheets
- understand and explain why spreadsheets are used in the day to day work of accountants
- construct a multi-sheet cash flow projection statement using appropriate formatting, formulae and links
- recalculate a multi-sheet cash flow projection statement using appropriate formatting, formulae and links
- acquire some knowledge of how to use spreadsheets to prepare a master budget.

This session looks at the role of spreadsheets in management accounting, their use, benefits and limitations. There is a number of spreadsheets on the market. Excel is the most widely used and this is the spreadsheet package used in this unit. This unit will not provide you with a full working knowledge of spreadsheets, but rather a basic knowledge.

6.1 The nature, benefits and limitations of spreadsheets and the use of spreadsheets in accounting

A spreadsheet is a tool for calculating, analysing and manipulating figures. It makes calculations quicker and easier and is used for sorting, filtering and categorising large volumes of information.

6.1.1 The benefits and limitations of spreadsheets

Spreadsheets have the following benefits and limitations.

Benefits

- They are easy to learn and use.
- Calculation and the manipulation of data are easier and quicker than carrying it out manually.
- They can be used to analyse financial information, and help with the reporting and sharing of it.
- They enable 'what if' analyses to be carried out very quickly.

Limitations

- The end result is only as good as the original data entered.
- Formulae are hidden so the logic underlying the calculations may not be obvious.
- They can easily be corrupted and it may be difficult to find errors in large or multi-sheet spreadsheets.

6.1.2   Why spreadsheets are used in the day to day work of accountants

Spreadsheets can be used in accounting to draw up all sorts of statements and prepare analyses including:

- budgets and forecasts
- revenue analysis
- cost analysis
- reconciliations
- income statements
- balance sheets
- break-even analysis.

6.2 The fundamentals of spreadsheets

A spreadsheet can be thought of as an electronic piece of paper (worksheet) divided into columns which are numbered A, B, C, etc., and rows which are numbered 1, 2, 3, etc. Where a column intersects with a row is called a cell. Each cell has an address, for example, the cell A1 is where column A intersects with row 1. The cell the cursor is in is called the active cell.

The formula bar enables you to see the contents of the active cell and also shows the address of the active cell.

The following is an example of a partly completed cash flow spreadsheet.

B6	▾	*fx*	2300

	A	B	C	D	E
1	A partly completed spreadsheet				
2					
3		January	February	March	Total
4		£	£	£	£
5	Receipts				
6	Food	2,300	2,150	2,450	
7	Drink	7,540	6,950	8,520	
8	Total				
9					
10	Payments				
11	Purchases	3,000	3,200	2,950	
12	Wages	2,850	2,850	2,850	
13	Rent			3,000	
14	Overheads	745	850	950	
15	Drawings	1,000	1,250	1,500	
16	Total				
17					
18	Net cash flow				

A spreadsheet contains the following.

- Text. A text cell usually contains words, although it may also contain symbols and numbers that do not form part of a calculation. In this case an apostrophe should be inserted before the number, for example, '621.

- Values. A value is a number that can or will be used in a calculation.
- Formulae. Entering a formula will enable a calculation to be carried out on the values in other cells, the result of which will appear in the cell containing the formula. Note that the formula will remain in the background. When values in the spreadsheet are changed, the spreadsheet automatically updates itself.

6.2.1   Spreadsheet formulae

All formulae start by inputting an equals sign =. However the rest of the formula needs to be entered in a particular way as detailed below.

- *Addition*: to add the January receipts together in the above spreadsheet, input =B6+B7 into cell B8. To add a number of figures together such as the January payments, input =Sum(B11:B15) into cell B16. Likewise to add all the sales together, enter =Sum(B8:D8) into cell E8.
- *Subtraction*: to subtract one figure from another, such as the total of January payments from the total of January receipts, input =B8–B16 into cell B18.
- *Multiplication*: the symbol * is used instead of the usual multiplication sign ($\times$), for example, inputting =G5*8 will multiply the value in cell G5 by the number 8.
- *Division*: the symbol / is used instead of the division sign ($\div$), for example, =G6/2 will divide the value in cell G6 by the number 2.
- *Powers*: to raise to a power, either use the ^ symbol, for example, =4^2 or use =Power(4,2). Both will give you 4 to the power of 2, or 4^2.
- *Square root*: to find the square root of 4 either use =4^(1/2) or =SQRT(4).
- *Brackets* should be used to show the order of calculation. Therefore, the formula =(G7+G8+G9)/5 denotes that the additions are to be performed first and then the division. If the brackets were missing, the value in G9 would be divided by 5 and then the other two values would be added to it.
- *Rounding*: to round individual numbers, use the formula: =Round(number,digit) where 'number' refers to the figure to be rounded and 'digit' refers to the number of decimal places to which the number is to be rounded.

6.2.2   Formatting spreadsheets

Most spreadsheets, including Excel, have a formula bar from which a number of operations can be performed. If the formula bar is not visible when you open a spreadsheet, choose *View*, *Formula bar*. Below are listed a number of useful operations. However, do take the time to play with different operations.

- Headings. In accountancy, as in other fields, headings are important to tell the reader what the document is about. Therefore it is important to give each spreadsheet a heading.
- Changing the font size, colour of the text or adding shading. This works in the same way as for a number of word-processing packages, including Word.

- Column width. Using the spreadsheet toolbar, go to **Format** then **Column** then **Width**. This will enable you to set (to the desired width) the column or columns in which the cursor is placed. Consider whether it will look neater if the columns in your table are of the same width.

- Aligning information. To help users read your spreadsheet it is important to right align columns of figures.

- Wrapping text. If text is entered in a cell which fits the width of the cell, then it will be shown normally. If the text does not fit and nothing has been entered in the cell to the right of the cell containing the text, then that text will appear across the spreadsheet. If, however, text is entered that does not fit into the cell and the cell immediately to the right also has something in it, then the text will not be fully shown. To prevent this problem, the wrapping text function can be used. Select the cells you want to format. Using the spreadsheet toolbar go to **Format**, click **Cells**, and then click the **Alignment** tab. Under **Text control**, select the **Wrap text** check box.

- Setting the number specification. There will be cases when figures will need to be shown to a particular number of decimal places, such as when calculating ratios to two decimal places. Select the cells you want to format, from the spreadsheet toolbar go to **Format**, click **Cells** and then click the **Number** tab. Enter the number of decimal places you want to display. (Also have a look at some of the other categories listed on this *Number* tab such as *Currency, Accounting, Percentage* and *Scientific*.)

- Formatting figures to show negative numbers in brackets. Accountants normally show negative figures in brackets. Excel does not have a pre-set format but you can format cells from the toolbar. As per Figure 71, go to **Format**, click **Cells** and then from the **Number** tab choose **Custom** which will show you several lines of code in the **Type** box. Find the line that says '_-*#, ##0_-;-*#,##0_-;_-*"-"_-;_-@_-', near the bottom of the list. This shows you how Excel displays the contents of a cell. If you look carefully, you can see that there are four blocks of characters separated by semicolons (;). The blocks are (1) positive numbers, (2) negative numbers, (3) nil and (4) text. The second block ;-*#, ##0_-; is the interesting one, which, as it stands, will show a negative figure preceded by a minus sign at the right-hand edge of the cell. To change this appearance to brackets all you need to do is:

  (a) In the Type box type a left bracket sign (in place of the - at the start of the block.

  (b) Type a single right bracket sign) in place of the _ and the - at the end of the block. You have to replace two characters to ensure that columns of figures are in the correct vertical alignment with the right bracket outside of the column.

     You can do this either in a single cell or more commonly by highlighting a block of cells before you go to **Format, Cells**.

- *Taking figures from another worksheet*

  In Excel a formula that refers to another cell contains references to that cell and, where relevant, to the worksheet in which the cell appears. For example, to show in a cell the contents of cell B20 within the current worksheet, the formula would appear

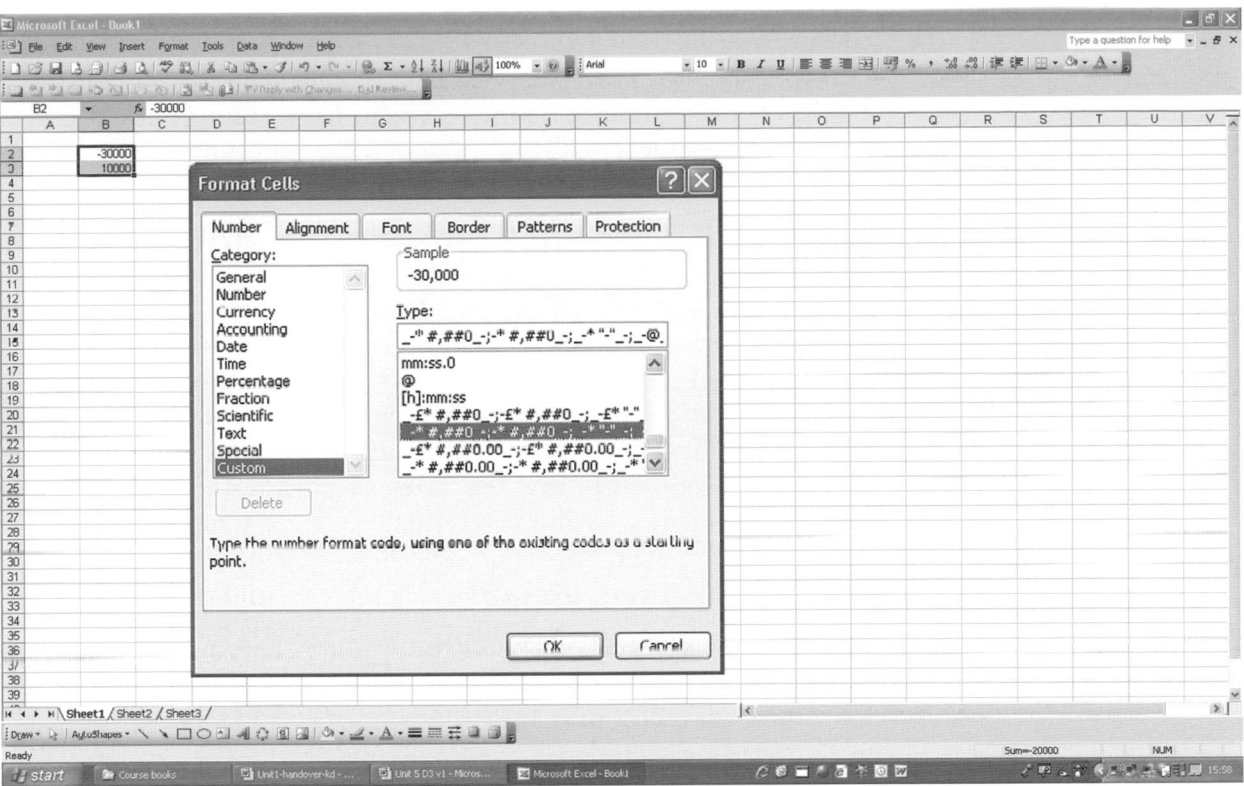

Figure 71 Negative numbers spreadsheet

as = B20 or = + B20. If the reference is to another worksheet within the same workbook, the reference includes the name of the other worksheet. For example, to show the contents of cell B20 which is in another worksheet called 'January' the formula would appear as = 'January'! B20.

- *Relevant and absolute references*

  Excel cell references can be relative or absolute. The normal situation is that references are relative. If cell B5 contains a reference to cell D7, what this tells us is to look two columns to the right (B to D) and two rows down (5 to 7). If you copy the contents of B5 down 10 rows to B15, the reference will have changed to D17 (which relatively is the same position right two/down two).

  At times you will want to copy a formula but still refer to a fixed cell. For example, if you are presenting data about monthly transactions and the name of the month is shown in cell A1 (which shows, say, October), then it can be useful to show October at different points in your report without having to change them manually, if you then use the same spreadsheet as the basis for your November report. Excel allows you to have a fixed cell reference. This appears as $A$1, which, if copied to another position on the worksheet, will always refer back to cell A1. You include the reference either by typing the $ signs or by typing A1 and then pressing Function key F4.

  If you experiment with this you may notice that if you press F4 repeatedly it is a toggle which shows A1, $A$1, A$1, $A1, A1, and so on. This gives you the choice of the following:

  A1   Relative reference

  $A$1   Fixed reference always refer to fixed cell

A$1   Fixed reference always refer to fixed row but relative column

$A1   Fixed reference always refer to fixed column but relative row

6.3 Constructing a multi-sheet cash flow projection statement

Spreadsheet packages, such as Excel, allow the accountant to work with a number of worksheets that relate to each other and share common information. For example, if a company has different regions or different product lines, a separate worksheet can be prepared for each region or product line and the figures from each can be combined in yet another sheet showing the totals.

6.3.1 Naming worksheets

In Excel a file is known as a **workbook** and consists of one or more **worksheets**. Typically, a new file starts with three blank worksheets named sheet 1, sheet 2 and sheet 3.

When using multiple sheets, it is wise to name your sheets. This can be done in two ways:

1 choose **Format>Sheets>Rename** to name the current sheet; or (the easier way)
2 double click on the sheet tab you wish to rename, and type over the highlighted area.

6.3.2 Inserting extra worksheets

To insert an extra worksheet in a workbook, choose **Insert>Worksheet**. This will place a new worksheet in front of the current one. You can change the order of worksheets within a workbook either by dragging the tab of the worksheet to be moved to its new position, or by right clicking on a tab and choosing the **Move or Copy** option. This option also enables you to insert a copy of an existing spreadsheet, which can be useful if you wish to create a spreadsheet which is similar to an existing one.

6.3.3 Grouping worksheets

Excel allows you to group spreadsheets by right clicking on a tab and choosing the **Select All Sheets** option. This selects the group mode in which changing cell B5 in one worksheet changes the same cell in all the other sheets. This can be useful if, for example, you need to change the headings on each sheet, but it should be used with caution in case you overwrite something unintentionally. To get out of group mode, right click a tab and choose **Ungroup Sheets**.

6.3.4 Linking workbooks together

To link data from one workbook to another, use **Paste Special** in the following way.

1 Highlight the appropriate range of cells.
2 Copy these cells using **Copy** from the **Edit** menu (or use **Ctrl + C**).

3   Open the worksheet you wish to link to and select the appropriate cells.

4   From the *Edit* menu, select *Paste Special* which will bring up the *Paste Special* dialogue box.

5   Click the *Paste Link*.

In financial spreadsheets, it is common to have standard information that you may wish to change, for example, the rate of interest that is being charged on a bank overdraft. On a single sheet spreadsheet it would be usual to have the rate of interest shown in a single cell, say C3, and then for all the cells that make a calculation relating to the interest rate to refer to C3. In this way, if the interest rate changes, you need only change C3, not each cell. In a multi-sheet spreadsheet, it is convenient to have a separate data sheet which includes the variable factors, usually with notes of any assumptions. Linking all of the individual sheets to a single source of information should improve the efficiency of spreadsheet creation and reduce the potential for error.

6.3.5   Example

In Unit 4 you saw the cash flow forecast for Prestige Bears Limited. This example shows how a multi-sheet spreadsheet can be used to produce a cash flow forecast using the data for Prestige Bears Limited.

The forecast sales volume is as follows:

	Volume	Selling price per unit
		£
Year 1		
1st quarter	1,000	65
2nd quarter	1,100	65
3rd quarter	1,200	65
4th quarter	1,500	65
Year 2		
1st quarter	1,600	65

Each bear costs £16 in direct materials and £20 in direct labour. Production fixed overheads for year 1 are forecast to be £20,000 which includes depreciation of £2,000.

Prestige Bears is a new company and starts year 1 with non-current assets of £10,000 and a £10,000 overdraft.

Other information available is as follows.

●   Customers pay two months after the month of purchase.

●   The company has to pay suppliers within one month of the purchase of materials.

●   Closing inventory of materials is required to be 10% of the following quarter's sales.

From this information, a cash flow forecast can be created, but to do this, a budget for sales and one for costs must be prepared. You could show all of this information on one spreadsheet, but in practice the amount of information would be too much and the spreadsheet would be unwieldy and difficult to view or print. It is easier to separate the information into three separate worksheets. Sales and costs can then be calculated in their own worksheets and then linked to the cash flow.

When you start a cash flow or other model, you will be given some initial information and will make some key assumptions. It is convenient to put all of this information into a single worksheet. Using a data sheet as part of a multi-sheet spreadsheet has some very important advantages, as follows.

(a) Users of the spreadsheet only have one place to look for the key assumptions.

(b) If you link all references to a particular item, say, an assumed rate of interest, to one cell in a data sheet you can simply amend your assumption by changing the one cell in the data sheet rather than having to go through every worksheet and change the formulae.

(c) The likelihood of typing errors is reduced, particularly in complicated formulae.

(d) Using a data sheet also gives you an opportunity to explain some of your assumptions.

To help you follow this example, the preparation of the cash flow statement has been divided into a number of steps. Where formulae are used in preparing a worksheet, the worksheet is shown followed by the formula and some explanation. Note that you can see the formula in your worksheet by pressing **CTRL + `** *(grave accent).*

Step 1   Prepare the data sheet.

Taking the information for Prestige Bears, a data sheet could contain six sets of information:

(a) the heading

(b) sales volume and price data

(c) sales receipts

(d) inventory and cost data

(e) purchase payment data

(f) opening bank overdraft.

Step 1a   Enter the heading and also label the tab at the bottom left of the workbook with the appropriate title.

Type the top line in cell A1 (A is the column reference and 1 is the row reference)

Some columns have been made narrower than others to ensure that the spreadsheets fit on the page.

	A	B	C	D	E	F	G	H	I	J	K
1	**PRESTIGE BEARS LIMITED – MULTI-SHEET CASH FLOW EXAMPLE**										
2	**DATA SHEET**										
3											

Step 1b Enter the sales volume and price data.

	A	B	C	D	E	F	G	H	I	J	K
1	**PRESTIGE BEARS LIMITED – MULTI-SHEET CASH FLOW EXAMPLE**										
2	**DATA SHEET**										
3											
4	**Sales volume**				**Volume**		**Selling price**				
5							**per unit**				
6							£				
7	Year 1		1st quarter		1,000		65				
8			2nd quarter		1,100		65				
9			3rd quarter		1,200		65				
10			4th quarter		1,500		65				
11											
12	Year 2		1st quarter		1,600		65				
13											
	Sheet 1 Data sheet										

Step 1c Enter the sales receipts.

To calculate which month's sales revenues are received in a quarter, the quarter's sales need to be broken down into months and when they will be paid determined. Note that it is assumed that sales are spread evenly over the quarter.

	A	B	C	D	E	F	G	H	I	J	K
1	**PRESTIGE BEARS LIMITED – MULTI-SHEET CASH FLOW EXAMPLE**										
2	**DATA SHEET**										
3											
4	**Sales volume**				**Volume**		**Selling price**				
5							**per unit**				
6							£				
7	Year 1		1st quarter		1,000		65				
8			2nd quarter		1,100		65				
9			3rd quarter		1,200		65				
10			4th quarter		1,500		65				
11											
12	Year 2		1st quarter		1,600		65				
13											
14	**Sales receipts' assumption**										
15	*All customers pay two months after purchase*										
16											
17	**Sales in**		**are paid in**		*Example: Quarter 2 receipts represent (see * below)*						
18	Month 1		Month 3								
19	Month 2		Month 4		*Month 2*		*Q1 × $\frac{1}{3}$*		*Q1 × $\frac{2}{3}$*		
20	Month 3		Month 5		*Month 3*		*Q1 × $\frac{1}{3}$*				*0.6667 × Q1*
21	Month 4		Month 6		*Month 4*		*Q2 × $\frac{1}{3}$*		*Q2 × $\frac{1}{3}$*		*0.3333 × Q2*
22	Month 5		Month 7								
23	Month 6		Month 8								
24											
	Sheet 1 Data sheet										

* Month 2 and month 3 receipts are each assumed to be equal to one third of the sales in the first quarter. Month 4 receipts are assumed to be one third of the sales in the second quarter.

Step 1d   Enter the inventory and cost data.

	A	B	C	D	E	F	G	H	I	J	K
1	**PRESTIGE BEARS LIMITED – MULTI-SHEET CASH FLOW EXAMPLE**										
2	**DATA SHEET**										
3											
4	**Sales volume**				**Volume**		**Selling price**				
5							**per unit**				
6							£				
7	Year 1		1st quarter		1,000		65				
8			2nd quarter		1,100		65				
9			3rd quarter		1,200		65				
10			4th quarter		1,500		65				
11											
12	Year 2		1st quarter		1,600		65				
13											
14	**Sales receipts' assumption**										
15	*All customers pay two months after purchase*										
16											
17	**Sales in**		**are paid in**		*Example: Quarter 2 receipts represent*						
18	Month 1		Month 3								
19	Month 2		Month 4		*Month 2*		$Q1 \times \frac{1}{3}$		$Q1 \times \frac{2}{3}$		
20	Month 3		Month 5		*Month 3*		$Q1 \times \frac{1}{3}$				*0.6667*
21	Month 4		Month 6		*Month 4*		$Q2 \times \frac{1}{3}$		$Q2 \times \frac{1}{3}$		*0.3333*
22	Month 5		Month 7								
23	Month 6		Month 8								
24											
25	**Inventory**										
26	Closing inventory is		10%		of the next quarter's expected sales						
27											
28	**Costs of making each bear**										
29					£						
30	Direct materials				16						
31	Direct labour				20						
32											
33	Production overhead costs				20,000						
34	including depreciation of				2,000						
35											
	Sheet 1 Data sheet										

Step 1e   Enter the purchase payment data.

	A	B	C	D	E	F	G	H	I	J	K
1	**PRESTIGE BEARS LIMITED – MULTI-SHEET CASH FLOW EXAMPLE**										
2	**DATA SHEET**										
3											
4	**Sales volume**				**Volume**		**Selling price**				
5							**per unit**				
6							£				
7	Year 1		1st quarter		1,000		65				
8			2nd quarter		1,100		65				
9			3rd quarter		1,200		65				
10			4th quarter		1,500		65				
11											
12	Year 2		1st quarter		1,600		65				
13											
14	**Sales receipts' assumption**										
15	*All customers pay two months after purchase*										
16											
17	**Sales in**		**are paid in**		*Example: Quarter 2 receipts represent:*						
18	Month 1		Month 3								
19	Month 2		Month 4		*Month 2*		$Q1 \times \frac{1}{3}$		$Q1 \times \frac{2}{3}$		
20	Month 3		Month 5		*Month 3*		$Q1 \times \frac{1}{3}$				*0.6667*
21	Month 4		Month 6		*Month 4*		$Q2 \times \frac{1}{3}$		$Q2 \times \frac{1}{3}$		*0.3333*
22	Month 5		Month 7								
23	Month 6		Month 8								
24											
25	**Inventory**										
26	Closing inventory is		10%		of the next quarter's sales						
27											
28	**Costs of making each bear**										
29					£						
30	Direct materials				16						
31	Direct labour				20						
32											
33	Production overhead costs				20,000						
34	including depreciation of				2,000						
35											
36	**Purchase payments' assumption**										
37	*The company has to pay its suppliers within one month of the purchase of materials*										
38											
39	**Purchases in**		**are paid in**		*Quarter 2 payments represent*						
40	Month 1		Month 2								
41	Month 2		Month 3		*Month 3*		$Q1 \times \frac{1}{3}$		$Q1 \times \frac{1}{3}$		*0.3333*
42	Month 3		Month 4		*Month 4*		$Q2 \times \frac{1}{3}$				*0.6667*
43	Month 4		Month 5		*Month 5*		$Q2 \times \frac{1}{3}$		$Q2 \times \frac{2}{3}$		
44	Month 5		Month 6								
45	Month 6		Month 7								
46											
	Sheet 1 Data sheet										

Step 1f   Enter the opening bank overdraft to complete the data sheet.

	A	B	C	D	E	F	G	H	I	J	K
1	PRESTIGE BEARS LIMITED – MULTI-SHEET CASH FLOW EXAMPLE										
2	DATA SHEET										
3											
4	Sales Volume				Volume		Selling price				
5							per unit				
6							£				
7	Year 1		1st quarter		1,000		65				
8			2nd quarter		1,100		65				
9			3rd quarter		1,200		65				
10			4th quarter		1,500		65				
11											
12	Year 2		1st quarter		1,600		65				
13											
14	Sales receipts' assumption										
15	All customers pay two months after purchase										
16											
17	Sales in		are paid in		Example: Quarter 2 receipts represent:						
18	Month 1		Month 3								
19	Month 2		Month 4		Month 2		$Q1 \times \frac{1}{3}$		$Q1 \times \frac{2}{3}$		
20	Month 3		Month 5		Month 3		$Q1 \times \frac{1}{3}$				0.6667
21	Month 4		Month 6		Month 4		$Q2 \times \frac{1}{3}$		$Q2 \times \frac{1}{3}$		0.3333
22	Month 5		Month 7								
23	Month 6		Month 8								
24											
25	Inventory										
26	Closing inventory is		10%		of the next quarter's sales						
27											
28	Costs of making each bear										
29					£						
30	Direct materials				16						
31	Direct labour				20						
32											
33	Production overhead costs				20,000						
34	including depreciation of				2,000						
35											
36	Purchase payments' assumption										
37	The company has to pay its suppliers within one month of the purchase of materials										
38											
39	Purchases in		are paid in		Quarter 2 payments represent						
40	Month 1		Month 2								
41	Month 2		Month 3		Month 3		$Q1 \times \frac{1}{3}$		$Q1 \times \frac{1}{3}$		0.3333
42	Month 3		Month 4		Month 4		$Q2 \times \frac{1}{3}$				0.6667
43	Month 4		Month 5		Month 5		$Q2 \times \frac{1}{3}$		$Q2 \times \frac{2}{3}$		
44	Month 5		Month 6								
45	Month 6		Month 7								
46											
47	Opening balance sheet										
48	Consists of non-current assets and matching overdraft of										£10,000

Sheet 1 Data sheet

Step 2 On a separate worksheet calculate the cash received from sales.

From the information in the data sheet above, the cash received from sales can be calculated on a separate worksheet as follows:

	A	B	C	D	E	F
1	**PRESTIGE BEARS LIMITED**					
2	**CASH RECEIPTS/SALES REVENUE BUDGET**					
3						
4		**Year 1**				
5		**Q1**	**Q2**	**Q3**	**Q4**	**Total**
6		£	£	£	£	£
7	**Cash received from credit customers**					
8	From Q1 sales	21,667	43,333			65,000
9	From Q2 sales		23,833	47,667		71,500
10	From Q3 sales			26,000	52,000	78,000
11	From Q4 sales				32,500	32,500
12						
13	Total cash from credit customers	21,667	67,167	73,667	84,500	247,000
14						
15						
16	**Notes**					
17						
18	Sales volume	1,000	1,100	1,200	1,500	4,800
19						
20	Sales revenue	£65,000	£71,500	£78,000	£97,500	£312,000
	Sheet 2 Cash receipts					

The information in this budget is taken from the data sheet (see step 1f). This can be seen from looking at the formulae in the cells in the cash receipts/sales revenue budget. For example, in the following extract you can see how the figures link to the data sheet:

	A	B	C
4		**Year 1**	
5		**Q1**	**Q2**
6		£	£
7	**Cash received from credit customers**		
8	From Q1 sales	=+B20*'Data sheet'!K21	=+B20*'Data sheet'!K20
9	From Q2 sales		=+C20*'Data sheet'!K21
10	From Q3 sales		
11	From Q4 sales		
12			
13	Total cash from credit customers	=SUM(B8:B12)	=SUM(C8:C12)
14			
15			
16	**Notes**		
17			
18	Sales volume	=+'Data sheet'!E7	=+'Data sheet'!E8
19			
20	Sales revenue	=+B18*'Data sheet'!G7	=+C18*'Data sheet'!G8
	Sheet 2 Cash receipts		

Looking at the formula in cell B8 you can see that it takes the figure from cell B20, the sales revenue for Q1 of year 1 (£65,000) and multiplies it by cell K21 of the Data sheet tab (0.3333) to give the cash receipts from credit sales in quarter 1 of £21,667.

Remember that you can see the formulae in a worksheet by pressing CTRL + ` *(grave accent)*.

Step 3   On a separate worksheet show the cost budget information.

In a similar way, a spreadsheet for the cost budget information can be produced:

	A	B	C	D	E	F	G
1	PRESTIGE BEARS LIMITED – MULTI-SHEET CASH FLOW EXAMPLE						
2	COST BUDGET						
3							
4			Year 1				
5			Q1	Q2	Q3	Q4	Total
6							
7	Production budget		Units	Units	Units	Units	Units
8	Sales volume		1,000	1,100	1,200	1,500	4,800
9	Less: opening inventory		–	(110)	(120)	(150)	–
10			1,000	990	1,080	1,350	4,800
11	Add: closing inventory desired						
12	10%	of next Q sales	110	120	150	160	160
13							
14	Production required		1,110	1,110	1,230	1,510	4,960
15							
16	Production cost budget						
17							
18	Production required (units)		1,110	1,110	1,230	1,510	4,960
19			£	£	£	£	£
20	Direct materials costs		17,760	17,760	19,680	24,160	79,360
21	Direct labour costs		22,200	22,200	24,600	30,200	99,200
22	Production overheads		5,000	5,000	5,000	5,000	20,000
23							
24	Total production costs		44,960	44,960	49,280	59,360	198,560
25							
26	Payments to suppliers						
27			£	£	£	£	£
28	Materials for Q1		11,840	5,920			17,760
29	Materials for Q2			11,840	5,920		17,760
30	Materials for Q3				13,120	6,560	19,680
31	Materials for Q4					16,107	16,107
32							
33	Total payments to suppliers		11,840	17,760	19,040	22,667	71,307
	Sheet 3 Cost budget						

This information is also taken from the data sheet as the following extract shows:

	A	B	C	D
4			**Year 1**	
5			**Q1**	**Q2**
6				
7	**Production budget**		Units	Units
8	Sales volume		=+'Data sheet'!E7	=+'Data sheet'!E8
9	Less: opening inventory		0	=-C12
10			=+C8+C9	=+D8+D9
11	Add: closing inventory desired			
12	=+'Data sheet'!C26	of next Q sales	=+D8*$A$12	=+E8*$A$12
13				
14	Production required		=+C10+C12	=+D10+D12
	Sheet 3 Cost budget			

The user can see the percentage of sales used to calculate stock (10%) on the worksheet (at A12) and this figure is linked to the data sheet.

Step 4   The cash flow forecast.

The figures from the sales budget and cost budget worksheets are then brought together on the cash flow forecast worksheet:

	A	B	C	D	E	F
1	**PRESTIGE BEARS LIMITED – MULTI-SHEET CASH FLOW EXAMPLE**					
2	**CASH FLOW FORECAST**					
3						
4		**Year 1**				
5		**Q1**	**Q2**	**Q3**	**Q4**	**Total**
6		£	£	£	£	£
7	**Cash inflows**					
8	Cash received from sales	21,667	67,166	73,667	84,500	247,000
9						
10	**Cash outflows**					
11	Payments to suppliers	11,840	17,760	19,040	22,667	71,307
12	Wages	22,200	22,200	24,600	30,200	99,200
13	Production overheads (excluding depreciation)	4,500	4,500	4,500	4,500	18,000
14	Total cash payments	38,540	44,460	48,140	57,367	188,507
15						
16	Net cash inflows/(outflows)	(16,873)	22,706	25,527	27,133	58,493
17	Cash at start of quarter	(10,000)	(26,873)	(4,167)	21,360	
18						
19	Cash at end of quarter	(26,873)	(4,167)	21,360	48,493	
	Sheet 4 Cash flow forecast					

As the following extract shows, this worksheet uses information from the other sheets:

	A	B	C
4		**Year 1**	
5		**Q1**	**Q2**
6		£	£
7	**Cash inflows**		
8	Cash received from sales	=+'Sales budget'!B13	=+'Sales budget'!C13
9			
10	**Cash outflows**		
11	Payments to suppliers	=+'Costs budget'!C33	=+'Costs budget'!D33
12	Wages	=+'Costs budget'!C21	=+'Costs budget'!D21
13	Production overheads (excluding depreciation)	=+'Costs budget'!C22 -'Data sheet'!$E$34*0.25	=+'Costs budget'!D22 -'Data sheet'!$E$34*0.25
14	Total cash payments	=SUM(B11:B13)	=SUM(C11:C13)
15			
16	Net cash inflows/(outflows)	=+B8-B14	=+C8-C14
17	Cash at start of quarter	=-'Data sheet'!K48	=+B19
18			
19	Cash at end of quarter	=+B16+B17	=+C16+C17
	Sheet 4 Cash flow forecast		

The cash flow takes some information from the data sheet such as the opening cash balance and the depreciation included in production overheads (which have to be adjusted for as it is a non-cash item).

Activity 6.1   ....

See if you can recreate the above spreadsheets. You might also like to change some of the initial data and see how it changes the results given in the cash flow forecast.

Spend between 30 and 60 minutes doing this.

Feedback   ....

If you have worked through this example, you may have found it rather challenging but, hopefully, it will have given you an insight into how accountants use spreadsheets.

6.4 Using a multi-sheet spreadsheet to calculate master budgets

Multi-sheet spreadsheets can be used in budgeting. The following example shows the production of a multi-sheet spreadsheet that calculates a budgeted income statement, cash flow and balance sheet.

6.4.1 Example

This is a complex example, designed to help you in a work situation. How much time you spend looking at it will depend on your need. If you are merely studying this course for interest, then you may not wish to spend time on this example. However, if you are working in accountancy, you may find this example very relevant and will want to spend more time on it. Even if you do not want to work through this example as a spreadsheet exercise, it is a very useful example of budgeting and draws together material you have studied elsewhere in this module.

Outdoor Wear Limited is a company which manufactures clothing. For simplicity it is assumed that it only manufactures two products: trousers and jackets.

The information that is available is summarised in the following five tables. The objective is to calculate the budgeted income statement, cash flow and balance sheet from the information given. As a starting point, Tables 1 to 4 would form a data sheet together with the opening balance sheet as Table 5.

Table 1 Sales and production information

	Trousers	**Jackets**
Unit sales for the year	10,000	6,000
	£	£
Unit selling price	65	140
Unit variable costs:		
Direct material	19	34
Direct labour	14	28

Direct labour costs are based on an average wage of £15,500 per person per year.

Table 2 Information on other costs per annum

	£	
Rent of premises	22,500	
Production heat and light	12,625	
Production business rates	10,550	
Office staff salaries	83,525	
Directors' salaries	122,500	
Marketing and distribution	15%	of sales value

Table 3 Targets for working capital

Trade receivables at end of year	2	months' sales
Trade payables (for materials)	1	month's purchases
Inventory of raw materials	75%	of the next month's production
Inventory of finished goods	50%	of a month's production

Table 4   Capital budget plans

	£
It is planned to buy new sewing machines at the start of the year costing	26,400
These will replace old machines which will be sold for their book value of	3,250
and which originally cost	17,900
All machinery is depreciated on a straight-line basis at	20%

No depreciation is charged on an asset in the year of disposal. A full year's depreciation is charged in the year of an asset's acquisition

Table 5   The opening balance sheet at 31 December 20X6 was as follows:

	£	£
Equipment at cost		83,500
Accumulated depreciation		65,425
Net book value		18,075
Inventory of raw materials		
Trousers	4,218	
Jackets	8,364	
	12,582	
Inventory of finished goods		
Trousers	3,300	
Jackets	5,580	
	8,880	
Trade receivables	74,000	
Cash at bank	36,500	
	131,962	
Trade payables	28,500	
Net current assets		103,462
Total assets less current liabilities		121,537
Capital and reserves		
Called up share capital		25,000
Retained earnings		96,537
		121,537

As well as the budgeted income statement, cash flow and balance sheet, it will be necessary to create a number of other spreadsheets to calculate the components such as a budget for production overheads.

Figure 72 shows the budgets that make up the cash budget, budgeted income statement and the budgeted balance sheet.

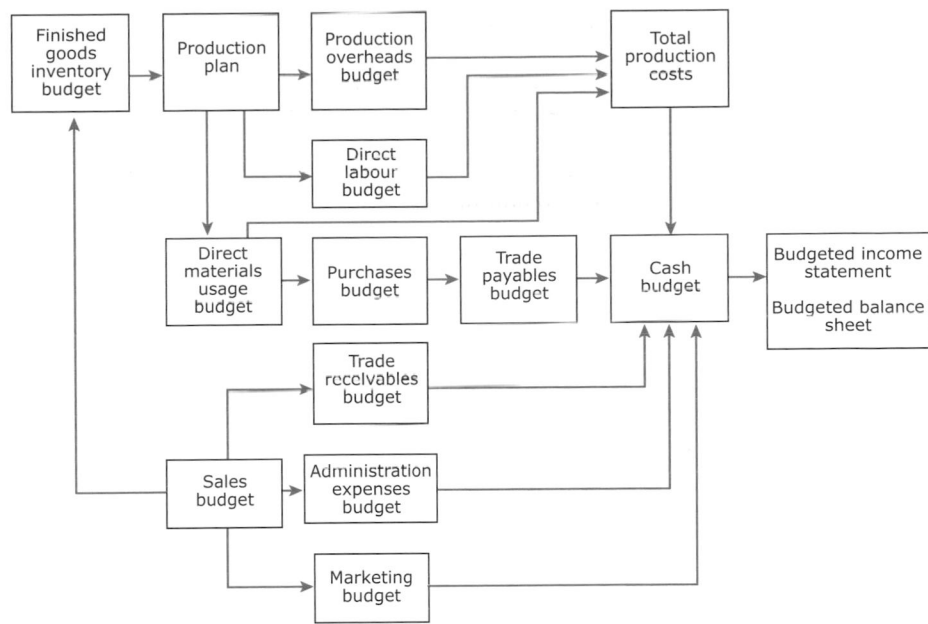

Figure 72   Budgets

Creating the budgeted income statement, cash flow and balance sheet for Outdoor Wear Limited ideally requires the use of a series of different spreadsheets to cover each stage of the calculations. These would be linked in a multi-sheet spreadsheet to the data contained in Tables 1 to 5. Potentially this gives a workbook with around 20 sheets but some of the sheets contain only a small amount of information and might in this case be combined with another page. In a real life example with more products, the amount of information will justify separate pages.

In all cases, the user of the workbook will be helped if the information is provided in clearly labelled worksheets which are linked logically back to the core information in the data sheet(s). It is useful to show on the worksheet where figures are taken from so that the reader can refer to the appropriate table. Do not forget that, although you may be looking at the workbook in Excel and can see where figures come from, someone else may be looking at a printed copy so will need the visible reference.

Our example of Outdoor Wear Limited could contain the following data sheet and a series of tables, each representing a single worksheet.

	A	B	C	D	E	F	G	H	I	J	K
1	**OUTDOOR WEAR LIMITED**										
2	**DATA SHEET**										
3											
4	Table 1	Sales and production information									
5							**Trousers**		**Jackets**		
6		Unit sales for the year					10,000		6,000		
7							£		£		
8		Unit selling price					65		140		
9		Unit variable costs:									
10		Direct material					19		34		
11		Direct labour					14		28		
12											
13		Direct labour costs are based on an average wage of £15,500 per person per year									
14											
15	Table 2	Information on other costs per annum									
16									£		
17		Rent of premises							22,500		
18		Production heat and light							12,625		
19		Production business rates							10,550		
20		Office staff salaries							83,525		
21		Directors' salaries							122,500		
22		Marketing and distribution							15%		of sales value
23											
24	Table 3	Targets for working capital									
25											
26		Trade receivables at end of year					2		months' sales		
27		Trade payables (for materials)					1		month's purchases		
28		Inventory of raw materials					75%		of the next month's production		
29		Inventory of finished goods					50%		of a month's production		
30											
31	Table 4	Capital budget plans									
32											£
33		It is planned to buy new sewing machines at the start of the year costing									26,400
34		These will replace old machines to be sold for their book value of									3,250
35		and which originally cost									17,900
36											
37		All machinery is depreciated on a straight-line basis at									20%
38											
39											
	Data sheet										

	A	B	C	D	E	F	G	H	I	J
1	**OUTDOOR WEAR LIMITED**									
2	**Sales budget**									
3										
4						**Trousers**		**Jackets**		**Total**
5	Unit sales for the year			*Table 1*		10,000		6,000		
6										
7	Unit selling price			*Table 1*		£65		£140		
8										
9	Total sales					£650,000		£840,000		£1,490,000
10										
11										
12										
	Sheet 1 Sales budget									

	A	B	C	D	E	F	G	H	I	J
1	**OUTDOOR WEAR LIMITED**									
2	**Trade receivables budget**									
3										
4						**Trousers**		**Jackets**		**Total**
5						£		£		£
6	Total sales			*Sheet 1*		650,000		840,000		1,490,000
7										
8	Trade receivables at end of year				2 months' sales					
9					divided by 6					
10										
11	Trade receivables at year end					108,333		140,000		248,333
12										
13										
14										
	Sheet 2 Trade receivables budget									

	A	B	C	D	E	F	G	H	I	J
1	**OUTDOOR WEAR LIMITED**									
2	**Production plan (units)**									
3										
4						**Trousers**		**Jackets**		
5										
6	Planned sales volume			*Table 1*		10,000		6,000		
7										
8	Add: closing inventory			*Table 3*		416		250		
9										
10	Less: opening inventory			*Sheet 10*		(100)		(90)		
11										
12	Planned production for the year					10,316		6,160		
13										
14										
15										
	Sheet 3 Production plan (units)									

	A	B	C	D	E	F	G	H	I	J
1	**OUTDOOR WEAR LIMITED**									
2	**Purchases budget (units)**									
3										
4						**Trousers**		**Jackets**		
5										
6	Production volume			*Sheet 3*		10,316		6,160		
7										
8	Add: planned raw materials' inventory at end of year					645		385		
9						*75%*	*of*	*75%*	*of*	
10						*10,316/12*		*6,160/12*		
11										
12	Less: raw materials' inventory at start of year					(222)		(246)		
13				*see below*						
14	Planned purchases of raw materials					10,739		6,299		
15										
16						£		£		
17	Raw materials' inventory at start of year (value)					4,218		8,364		
18				*Table 5*						
19										
20	Material cost per unit			*Table 1*		19		34		
21										
22	Opening inventory (units)					222		246		
23										
24										
25	Raw materials' inventory at end of year (value)									
26										
27	Closing inventory (units)			*see above*		645		385		
28										
29	Material cost per unit			*Table 1*		£19		£34		
30										
31	Closing inventory (value)					£12,255		£13,090		£25,345
32										
33										
34										
	Sheet 4 Purchases budget (units)									

	A	B	C	D	E	F	G	H	I	J
1	**OUTDOOR WEAR LIMITED**									
2	**Purchases budget (£s)**									
3										
4			Trade payables			**Trousers**		**Jackets**		**Total**
5										
6	Planned purchases (units)			*Sheet 4*		10,739		6,299		
7										
8	Cost per unit			*Table 1*		£19		£34		
9										
10	Total purchase costs					£204,041		£214,166		£418,207
11										
12										
13										
	Sheet 5 Purchases budget (£s)									

	A	B	C	D	E	F	G	H	I	J
1	**OUTDOOR WEAR LIMITED**									
2	**Trade payables**									
3										
4										
5		1 month's purchases *Sheet 5*				418,207/12				£34,851
6										
7										
8										
	Sheet 6 Trade payables									

	A	B	C	D	E	F	G	H	I	J
1	**OUTDOOR WEAR LIMITED**									
2	**Labour budget (£s)**									
3										
4						**Trousers**		**Jackets**		**Total**
5										
6	Planned production (units)			*Sheet 3*		10,316		6,160		
7										
8	Cost per unit			*Table 1*		£14		£28		
9										
10	Total labour costs					£144,424		£172,480		£316,904
11										
12										
13										
	Sheet 7 Labour budget (£s)									

	A	B	C	D	E	F	G	H	I	J
1	**OUTDOOR WEAR LIMITED**									
2	**Direct material costs of goods sold**									
3										
4						**Trousers**		**Jackets**		**Total**
5										
6	Production (units)			*Sheet 3*		10,000		6,000		
7										
8	Material cost per unit			*Table 1*		£19		£34		
9										
10	Material cost of goods to be sold					£190,000		£204,000		£394,000
11										
12										
13										
	Sheet 8 Direct material costs of goods sold									

	A	B	C	D	E	F	G	H	I	J
1	**OUTDOOR WEAR LIMITED**									
2	**Direct labour cost**									
3										
4						**Trousers**		**Jackets**		**Total**
5										
6	Production (units)			*Table 1*		10,000		6,000		
7										
8	Labour cost per unit			*Table 1*		£14		£28		
9										
10	Labour cost of goods to be sold					£140,000		£168,000		£308,000
11										
12										
13										
	Sheet 9 Direct labour cost									

	A	B	C	D	E	F	G	H	I	J
1	**OUTDOOR WEAR LIMITED**									
2	**Inventory of finished goods**									
3										
4						**Trousers**		**Jackets**		**Total**
5						£		£		£
6	Material cost per unit			*Table 1*		19		34		
7	Labour cost per unit			*Table 1*		14		28		
8	Total cost per unit					33		62		
9										
10	Closing inventory (units)			*Sheet 3*		416		250		
11										
12	Closing inventory (value)					£13,728		£15,500		£29,228
13										
14	Opening inventory (value)			*Table 5*		£3,300		£5,580		£8,880
15										
16	Opening inventory (units)					100		90		
17										
18										
19										
	Sheet 10 Inventory of finished goods									

	A	B	C	D	E	F	G	H	I	J
1	**OUTDOOR WEAR LIMITED**									
2	**Production overhead budget**									
3										
4								£		£
5	Production heat and light					*Table 2*				12,625
6	Production business rates					*Table 2*				10,550
7	Depreciation (see below)									18,400
8	Total									41,575
9										
10										
11	**Equipment**									
12	Opening cost of equipment					*Table 5*		83,500		
13	Disposals							(17,900)		
14								65,600		
15	Additions							26,400		
16	Closing cost							92,000		
17										
18	Depreciation rate		20%		straight-line			18,400		
19										
20										
21										
	Sheet 11 Production overhead budget									

	A	B	C	D	E	F	G	H	I	J
1	**OUTDOOR WEAR LIMITED**									
2	**Total production cost budget**									
3										
4										£
5	Direct materials					*Sheet 8*				394,000
6	Direct labour					*Sheet 9*				308,000
7	Production overheads					*Sheet 11*				41,575
8	Total									743,575
9										
10										
11										
	Sheet 12 Total production cost budget									

	A	B	C	D	E	F	G	H	I	J
1	**OUTDOOR WEAR LIMITED**									
2	**Administration expenses budget**									
3										£
4	Rent of premises					*Table 2*				22,500
5	Directors' salaries					*Table 2*				122,500
6	Office staff salaries					*Table 2*				83,525
7	Total									228,525
8										
9										
10										
	Sheet 13 Administration expenses budget									

	A	B	C	D	E	F	G	H	I	J
1	**OUTDOOR WEAR LIMITED**									
2	**Marketing expenses budget**									
3										
4	15%	of sales (sheet 1), i.e.,		15%	of			£1,490,000		£223,500
5										
6										
7										
	Sheet 14 Marketing expenses budget									

These worksheets are then used to produce the final product, the budgeted income statement, cash flow and balance sheet for Outdoor Wear Limited which are contained in the final three sheets, as follows.

	A	B	C	D	E	F	G	H	I	J
1	**OUTDOOR WEAR LIMITED**									
2	**Budgeted income statement for the year ended 31 December 20X7**									
3										
4						**Trousers**		**Jackets**		**Total**
5						£		£		£
6	Total sales			*Sheet 1*		650,000		840,000		1,490,000
7	Materials cost			*Sheet 8*		190,000		204,000		394,000
8	Labour cost			*Sheet 9*		140,000		168,000		308,000
9										
10	Total variable cost					330,000		372,000		702,000
11	Contribution					320,000		468,000		788,000
12	**% on sales**					*49.2%*		*55.7%*		*52.9%*
13	Production overhead			*Sheet 12*						41,575
14	Gross profit									746,425
15										
16	Administration costs			*Sheet 13*						228,525
17	Marketing costs			*Sheet 14*						223,500
18										
19	Net profit									294,400
20										
21										
22										
	Sheet 15 Budgeted income statement									

	A	B	C	D	E	F	G	H	I	J
1	**OUTDOOR WEAR LIMITED**									
2	**Budgeted cash flow statement for the year ended 31 December 20X7**									
3										
4								£		£
5	Cash to be collected from customers					*Note 1*				1,315,667
6										
7	Cash to be paid to suppliers					*Note 2*		411,856		
8	Direct labour					*Sheet 7*		316,904		
9	Heat and light					*Sheet 11*		12,625		
10	Business rates					*Sheet 11*		10,550		
11	Rent of premises					*Sheet 13*		22,500		
12	Directors' salaries					*Sheet 13*		122,500		
13	Office staff salaries					*Sheet 13*		83,525		
14	Marketing costs					*Sheet 14*		223,500		
15										
16										(1,203,960)
17	Net cash inflow from operations									111,707
18										
19	New equipment to be purchased					*Table 4*		26,400		
20	Proceeds of sale of old equipment					*Table 4*		(3,250)		
21										(23,150)
22	Net cash inflow									88,557
23										
24	Cash balance at beginning of year					*Table 5*				36,500
25	Cash balance at end of year									125,057
26										
28										
29	**Notes re cash flow**									
30										
31	Note 1: Cash to be collected from customers									
32										£
33	Sales during the period							*Sheet 1*		1,490,000
34	Less: credit sales unpaid at the end of the year							*Sheet 2*		(248,333)
35										
36										1,241,667
37	Add: cash collections from customers owed at the start of the year							*Table 5*		74,000
38	Cash to be collected from customers									1,315,667
39										
40	Note 2: Cash to be paid to suppliers									
41										£
42	Purchases during the period							*Sheet 5*		418,207
43	Less: credit purchases which remain payable at the end of the year							*Sheet 6*		(34,851)
44										
45										383,356
46	Add: cash to be paid to suppliers owed at the start of the year							*Table 5*		28,500
47	Cash to be paid to suppliers									411,856
48										
	Sheet 16 Budgeted cash flow statement									

	A	B	C	D	E	F	G	H	I	J
1	**OUTDOOR WEAR LIMITED**									
2	**Budgeted balance sheet at 31 December 20X7**									
3										
4								31 Dec 20X7		31 Dec 20X6
5						£		£		£
6	Equipment at cost			*Sheet 11*				92,000		83,500
7	Accumulated depreciation			*Note 1*				69,175		65,425
8	Net book value							22,825		18,075
9										
10	Inventory of raw materials									
11	Trousers			*Sheet 4*		12,255				4,218
12	Jackets			"		13,090				8,364
13						25,345				12,582
14	Inventory of finished goods									
15	Trousers			*Sheet 10*		13,728				3,300
16	Jackets			"		15,500				5,580
17						29,228				8,880
18	Trade receivables			*Sheet 2*		248,333				74,000
19	Cash at bank			*Sheet 16*		125,057				36,500
20						427,963				131,962
21										
22	Trade payables			*Sheet 6*		34,851				28,500
23										
24	Net current assets							393,112		103,462
25	Total assets less current liabilities							415,937		121,537
26										
27	Capital and reserves									
28	Called up share capital			*Table 5*				25,000		25,000
29	Retained earnings			*Note 2*				390,937		96,537
30								415,937		121,537
31										
32										
33										
	Sheet 17 Budgeted balance sheet									

	A	B	C	D	E	F	G	H	I	J
1	**OUTDOOR WEAR LIMITED**									
2	**Notes re balance sheet**									
3										
4	Note 1: Accumulated depreciation									
5								£		£
6	Depreciation at beginning of year					*Table 5*				65,425
7	Less: eliminated on disposals during year									
8	Cost of equipment sold					*Table 4*		17,900		
9	Book value of equipment sold					*Table 4*		3,250		
10	Accumulated depreciation on equipment sold									14,650
11										50,775
12	Depreciation for the current year							*Sheet 11*		18,400
13	Depreciation at end of year									69,175
14										
15	Note 2: Retained earnings									
16										
17	At start of year							*Table 5*		96,537
18	Add: profit for the year							*Sheet 15*		294,400
19										
20	At end of year									390,937
21										
22	NB: For simplicity taxation is ignored									
23										
	Notes re balance sheet									

Summary

In this session the nature, benefits and limitations of spreadsheets were discussed, as well as how they can be used in the day to day work of accountants. You saw an example of a spreadsheet and its contents and formulae and were shown how to construct a multi-sheet cash flow projection statement using an Excel spreadsheet. Finally, you saw how to construct a multi-sheet spreadsheet in order to prepare a master budget.

Having worked through the examples, you will have increased your knowledge of spreadsheet preparation and understood the potential uses of spreadsheets by management accountants.

Unit summary

Well done: you have now completed Unit 5.

You should now have an understanding of some of the various quantitative techniques employed by management accountants. Accountants are often seen as experts in such techniques and, in many organisations, are expected to assist in such calculations, even when the calculations are not dealing with purely financial data.

There were six sessions in Unit 5.

In **Session 1** you learned, or revised, how to perform basic numerical calculations.

Session 2 showed you how to use tables, graphs and frequency distributions to summarise and present data. You learned how to describe and use measures of centrality, including mean, median and mode, to analyse data. You also learned how to describe and use measures of dispersion, including variance, standard deviation and coefficient of variation.

Session 3 explained how to analyse the relationships between data using correlation and regression and how to use time series analysis to reveal a trend masked by seasonal fluctuations.

Session 4 showed you how to perform basic probability calculations. The session also explained how to use expected values in simple decision making situations and discussed the limitations of expected value techniques. Session 4 explained the nature of normal distribution curves and how to use normal distribution tables. You learned to understand and explain the concept of risk and uncertainty in terms of management decision making.

In **Session 5** you learned how the concept of the time value of money can be applied to short- and long-term decisions. The session showed you how to calculate future values of an investment using both simple and compound interest. Session 5 also showed you how to calculate the financial viability of a capital investment proposal by using the accounting rate of return, payback, the net present value and the internal rate of return; how to explain the relative merits of each approach; and how to explain the practical considerations surrounding capital investment appraisal. Session 5 also described some of the non-financial factors that can influence the capital investment decision process.

Session 6 showed you how to use spreadsheets to construct multi-sheet cash flow projection statements and master budgets. The session explained why spreadsheets are used in the day to day work of accountants and the benefits and limitations of spreadsheets.

Before moving on to Unit 6, please ensure that you have completed all the self-assessment questions and checked your answers with those provided.

Self-assessed Questions

The following questions are designed to allow you to test your understanding of what you have learned in Unit 5.

Question 1

From the following weekly sales figures, which of the two supermarkets has shown the greater relative variability of demand for the week?

Transaction value (£)	Number of transactions	
Demand (£)	A	B
Under 20	15	43
20 to under 40	25	99
40 to under 60	40	54
60 to under 80	108	40
80 to under 100	92	14
100 and over	20	10
	300	260

Suggested answer

f multiplied by $(x - \bar{x})^2$ gives $f(x - \bar{x})^2$

Supermarket A

Demand	x	f	fx	$x - \bar{x}$	$(x - \bar{x})^2$	$f(x - \bar{x})^2$
Under 20	10	15	150	−59.8	3,576.04	53,640.60
20–40	30	25	750	−39.8	1,584.04	39,601.00
40–60	50	40	2,000	−19.8	392.04	15,681.60
60–80	70	108	7,560	0.2	0.04	4.32
80–100	90	92	8,280	20.2	408.04	37,539.68
100–120	110	20	2,200	40.2	1,616.04	32,320.80
	360	300	20,940	−58.8	7,576.24	178,788.00

Calculate the standard deviation

$$\sqrt{\frac{\sum f(x - \bar{x})^2}{\sum f}} = \sqrt{\frac{178,788}{300}} = 24.41 \text{ (to 4 significant figures)}$$

Calculate the mean

$$\bar{x} = \frac{\sum fx}{\sum f} = \frac{20,940}{300} = 69.8$$

Coefficient of variation

$$= \frac{\sigma}{\bar{x}} \times 100 = \frac{24.41}{69.8} \times 100 = 34.97 \text{ (to 4 significant figures)}$$

Supermarket B

Demand	x	f	fx	$x - \bar{x}$	$(x - \bar{x})^2$	$f(x - \bar{x})^2$
Under 20	10	43	430	−33.3	1,108.89	47,682.27
20–40	30	99	2,970	−13.3	176.89	17,512.11
40–60	50	54	2,700	6.7	44.89	2,424.06
60–80	70	40	2,800	26.7	712.89	28,515.60
80–100	90	14	1,260	46.7	2,180.89	30,532.46
100–120	110	10	1,100	66.7	4,448.89	44,488.90
	360	260	11,260	100.2	8,673.34	171,155.40

Calculate the standard deviation

$$\sqrt{\frac{\sum f(x - \bar{x})^2}{\sum f}} = \sqrt{\frac{171,155.40}{260}} = 25.66 \text{ (to 4 significant figures)}$$

Calculate the mean

$$\bar{x} = \frac{\sum fx}{\sum f} = \frac{11,260}{260} = 43.31$$

Coefficient of variation

$$= \frac{\sigma}{\bar{x}} \times 100 = \frac{25.66}{43.31} \times 100 = 59.25 \text{ (to 4 significant figures)}$$

The relative variability of the demand in Supermarket B is greater than for Supermarket A.

Question 2

A Belgian baby wear company is trying to carry out some planning for its future sales income. Live births in Belgium over the past three years are listed below. Assume the date is currently the end of 2008. The number of births is shown in thousands.

	Live births			
Year	**Quarter 1**	**Quarter 2**	**Quarter 3**	**Quarter 4**
	('000)	('000)	('000)	('000)
2006	162	163	164	150
2007	155	156	153	140
2008	151	150	147	137

(a) Find the basic trend (centred four-quarter moving average) and the seasonal variation.

(b) Calculate the average seasonal adjustment for each quarter using the additive method.

(c) By drawing a graph of the basic trend line, forecast the number of live births in Belgium for the first quarter of 2009.

Suggested answer

(a) The trend calculation is given in the following table.

Year	Q	Births ('000)	4 quarter moving total ('000)	4 quarter moving average ('000)	Trend (centred 4 quarter moving) average ('000)	Seasonal variation ('000)
2006	1	162				
	2	163				
			639	159.75		
	3	164			158.875	5.125
			632	158.00		
	4	150			157.125	(7.125)
			625	156.25		
2007	1	155			154.875	0.125
			614	153.5		
	2	156			152.250	3.750
			604	151.00		
	3	153			150.500	2.500
			600	150.00		
	4	140			149.250	(9.250)
			594	148.5		
2008	1	151			147.750	3.250
			588	147.00		
	2	150			146.625	3.375
			585	146.25		
	3	147				
	4	137				

(b) The seasonal adjustments can now be collected together and averaged.

Year	Quarter 1	Quarter 2	Quarter 3	Quarter 4
	('000)	('000)	('000)	('000)
2006			5.125	(7.125)
2007	0.125	3.750	2.500	(9.250)
2008	3.250	3.375		
Total	3.375	7.125	7.625	(16.375)
Average seasonal adjustment*	1.6875	3.5625	3.8125	(8.1875)
Corrected average	1.4688	3.3437	3.5938	(8.4063)

* The average seasonal variation should add up to zero over the four quarters. The difference is 0.875, this difference is adjusted over the four quarters.

(c) Assuming a continuation of the basic trend line, draw a graph and extrapolate it to 2009 and look at the 13th quarter from the start of the records. From the graph below, the estimate for the first quarter of 2009 is 140,000, which, after adjustment for the seasonal variation of +1,469, gives a forecast of 141,469 live births.

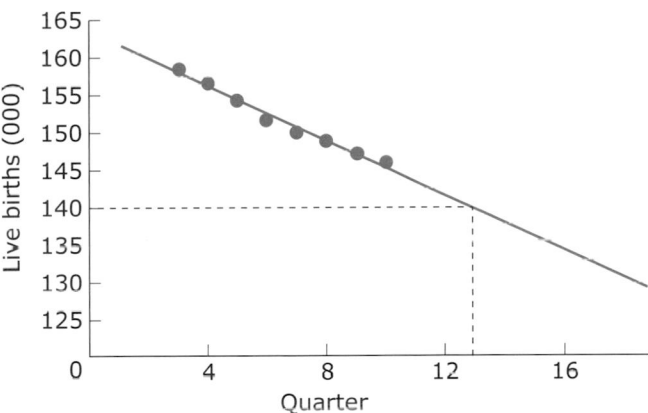

Figure 73 Extrapolated trend line

This estimate is from a hand-drawn graph. Using a spreadsheet to forecast the value, based on the basic trend data, produces an estimate of 140,196. Adjusting this for the seasonal adjustment of +1,469 gives an adjusted estimate of 141,665 live births.

You should consider which approach:

- you would find easier (which should be the spreadsheet)
- is likely to be more reliable (which should also be the spreadsheet)
- is likely to be more useful. (This depends on what the forecast is to be used for. Sometimes the objectivity of a spreadsheet may be preferable. However, a well-drawn line of best fit will normally, as shown in this example, produce an answer very close to that produced by more precise methods.)

Question 3

(i) Your building company is publicising its new apartment development. You take three photographs of each of the five rooms in the show flat and one exterior view.

(a) What is the probability that your marketing manager picks out the exterior photograph at random?

(b) Your public relations agent selects two photographs to use in your new brochure. What is the probability that they are both of the kitchen?

(c) The finance director wants to include one photograph in the year end report and accounts. What is the probability that it is of one of the two bedrooms?

(ii) A call centre sets a quality target of answering the telephone within 30 seconds. The results of monitoring show a normal distribution with an average answer time of 28 seconds and a standard deviation of 2 seconds.

    (a) What percentage of customers is still being kept waiting too long?

    (b) Would it be unusual to be kept waiting for more than 34 seconds?

Suggested Answer ....

(i) (a) $\frac{1}{16}$ (There are 16 photos in all, one of which is picked out.)

  (b) Three photographs are taken of each room, so on the first pick there is a $\frac{3}{16}$ chance of the photo being of the kitchen. Having picked the kitchen there is a $\frac{2}{15}$ chance of picking the kitchen again. This is an AND problem, therefore you should multiply the probabilities:

$$\frac{3}{16} \times \frac{2}{15} = \frac{1}{40} = 0.025 \text{ or } 2.5\%$$

  (c) This is an OR problem, therefore you should add the probabilities:

$$\frac{3}{16} + \frac{3}{16} = \frac{3}{8} = 0.375 \text{ or } 37.5\%$$

(ii) (a) Percentage of customers being kept waiting too long

    The following information is known:

    μ (average time) = 28 seconds; at this point $z = 0$

    x (quality target) = 30 seconds

    σ (standard deviation) = 2

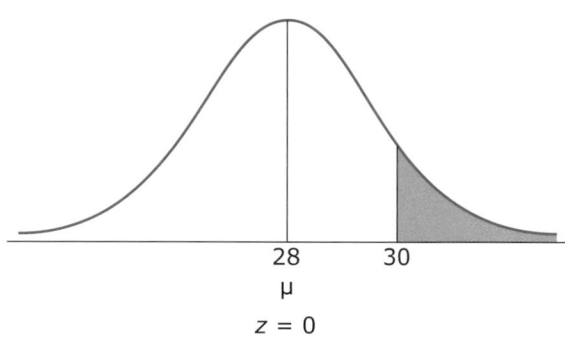

Figure 74   Area beyond 30 seconds

The shaded area represents the customers who are being kept waiting too long. The area between 28 and 30 seconds can be found as follows:

$$z = \frac{x - \mu}{\sigma} = \frac{30 - 28}{2} = 1$$

Using the tables, $z = 1$ corresponds to 0.3413, and to find the shaded area, deduct this figure from 0.5 to get 0.1587 or 15.87%. So 15.87% of customers are kept waiting too long.

  (b) Would it be unusual to be kept waiting for more than 34 seconds?

    x = a waiting time of 34 seconds

$$z = \frac{x - \mu}{\sigma} = \frac{34 - 28}{2} = 3$$

Using the tables, $z = 3$ corresponds to 0.4987. Deduct this from 0.5 to get 0.0013 or 0.13%.

So 0.13% of calls will be unanswered within 34 seconds. Put another way, 99.87% of all calls are answered within 34 seconds. It is, therefore, unlikely, but not impossible, to be kept waiting for more than 34 seconds.

Question 4 ....

A director of Kennington Machinery PLC has suggested to the Board of Directors that a new range of garden tools should be produced and sold. To produce the new range a machine costing £430,000 would have to be purchased.

The following figures have been presented to the Board, and you have noted that the analysis is on an accounting basis that reflects a profit figure which is subject to all sorts of adjustments.

Operating year	1	2	3	4
	£'000	£'000	£'000	£'000
Sales	345	410	480	500
Materials used:				
Opening inventory	50	40	50	60
Purchases	120	150	175	180
Closing inventory	(40)	(50)	(60)	–
Cost of materials used	130	140	165	240
Other costs:				
Labour	50	65	75	75
Other production costs	30	42	48	48
Selling and distribution costs	5	5	5	5
Administrative charge	15	15	15	15
Depreciation	100	100	100	100
Total of other costs	200	227	243	243
Profit	15	43	72	17

The following points have been made in the project proposal.

1 At the end of year 4 the machinery will be sold for £30,000.

2 Depreciation has been charged on a straight-line basis, calculated on a normal 4 year life for this sort of machine.

3 The company has £30,000 of materials in inventory, that would have no other use in the company and which could not be sold. The rest of the opening inventory would be purchased at the same time as the new machine. All other changes in inventory levels would occur at the end of the year.

4 Other production costs include a fixed overhead equal to 10% of the labour costs.

5 The administration charge is an apportionment of the company's existing fixed overheads.

6 Labour and other costs are incremental.

7 The company's weighted average cost of capital is 15%.

Calculate the net cash flow by working through the following steps. Work in whole thousands of pounds (£'000).

(a) Calculate the payback period.

(b) Calculate the net present value of the project. State clearly any assumptions that you make.

(c) As the marketing director thinks in terms of percentages rather than actual figures, calculate the internal rate of return.

(d) Describe how sensitivity analysis might be used to assist in assessing the project.

Suggested answer

Operating year		0	1	2	3	4
	Note	£'000	£'000	£'000	£'000	£'000
Machinery	1	(430)				30
Sales			345	410	480	500
Materials	3	(20)	(120)	(150)	(175)	(180)
Labour			(50)	(65)	(75)	(75)
Other production costs*			(25)	(35)	(40)	(40)
Selling and distribution			(5)	(5)	(5)	(5)
Net cash flow		(450)	145	155	185	230

* Figures are calculated in whole £'000.

Notes

1   The machinery will be purchased at the start of the project so will appear in year 0. The residual value of the machinery is £30,000 and will arise at the end of year 4.

2   Depreciation is not an incremental cash flow and is irrelevant.

3   Material inventory. Opening inventory – the original purchase price of £30,000 is irrelevant as it is a sunk cost. Only the incremental cost of new inventory is relevant. The rest of the opening inventory would be purchased at the same time as the new machine, so is shown in year 0.

4   Apportioned fixed overheads have been excluded from the analysis as they are irrelevant (they are not incremental cash flows).

5   It is assumed the all other costs arise at the end of the year.

6   When calculating NPV, the incremental cash flows should be discounted at the company's cost of capital of 15%.

(a) Calculating payback period:

Operating year	0	1	2	3	4
	£'000	£'000	£'000	£'000	£'000
Net cash flow	(450)	145	155	185	230
Cumulative cash flow	(450)	(305)	(150)	35	265
				▲	

Cash flows turn positive in year 3 so the project pays back during year 3.

$$\text{Payback time} = 2 \text{ years} + \frac{\text{negative balance outstanding at beginning}}{\text{cash inflow in payback year}} \times 12$$

$$= 2 \text{ years} + \frac{150{,}000}{185{,}000} \times 12 = 2 \text{ years } 9.73 \text{ months}$$

assuming that cash flows arise evenly during the years.

It would be usual to round up to 2 years 10 months.

Decision rule   Accept the project with the shortest payback period, although it cannot be used as the sole guide in the capital investment decision making process.

(b) Calculating NPV:

Operating year	0	1	2	3	4
	£'000	£'000	£'000	£'000	£'000
Net cash flow	(450)	145	155	185	230
Discount factor 15%	1.00	0.8696	0.7561	0.6575	0.5718
Present value	(450)	126	117	122	132
NPV (positive)	47				

(c) Calculating IRR:

NPV at 15% = £47,000 (from part (b)). Try 25%.

Operating year	0	1	2	3	4
	£'000	£'000	£'000	£'000	£'000
Net cash flow	(450)	145	155	185	230
Discount factor 25%	1.00	0.8000	0.6400	0.5120	0.4096
Present value	(450)	116	99	95	94
NPV	(46)				

$$\text{IRR} = 15 + 10 \times \frac{47}{47 + 46} = 20.05\%$$

(d) Sensitivity analysis

Carrying out sensitivity analysis involves looking at the individual expected cash flows, the duration of the project, and the cost of capital to see by how much each could change before the viability of the project would be affected. How sensitive is the NPV to individual cash flows, life of the project and cost of capital used? It is a way of showing the effect of uncertainty. Management can then decide whether the project would still be worthwhile.

Question 5 ....

Prepare a table that compares the four methods of investment appraisal covered in this unit.

Suggested answer ....

Comparison of project appraisal techniques

	Accounting rate of return	Payback	Net present value	Internal rate of return
Input	Accounting profits	Cash flows	Cash flows	Cash flows
Accounting adjustments	Yes	No	No	No
More than one definition	Yes	No	No	No
Discounted	No	Can be but not in this module	Yes	Yes
Need company cost of capital	No	No	Yes	No
More than one solution	No	No	No	Yes
Output	%	Years and months	£ Present value	%
Decision (single project)	Accept or reject	Additional discriminator rather than a sole guide	Accept if NPV is positive	Accept if IRR is higher than cost of capital
Decision (mutually exclusive projects)	Highest ARR	Shortest payback period; no clear decision rule if projects have same payback	Accept highest positive NPV	Accept highest IRR provided that it is higher than cost of capital
Problems	Does not take account of timing of cash flows (future benefits)	Ignores timing of cash flows and cash flow after the payback period	Assumes cash flows, other than initial, arise at end of year	Possible to have two IRRs for the same project or none
		No clear decision when projects have same payback period	Discount rate calculated on figures not known with certainty	Assumes that all project proceeds can be invested at rate of IRR
Positives		A crude measure of risk	Clear accept or reject decision	Do not have to have totally accurate cost of capital

Acknowledgements

Grateful acknowledgement is made to the following sources:

Figures

Pages 42–8 and 141: Copyright © Microsoft

Illustrations

Page 6: © www.casio.co.uk

Page 13: Copyright © Heather Clarke

Page 32: Copyright © 2010 by Sidney Harris. With permission from the author

Page 87: © iStockphoto.com, Duncan Walker

Page 88: © Pixmann, Alamy

Every effort has been made to contact copyright holders. If any have been inadvertently overlooked the publishers will be pleased to make the necessary arrangements at the first opportunity.